DEVELOPMENTS IN SEDIMENTOLOGY 11

INTRODUCTION TO PALEOLIMNOLOGY

DEVELOPMENTS IN SEDIMENTOLOGY 11

INTRODUCTION TO PALEOLIMNOLOGY

BY

C. C. REEVES Jr.

Department of Geosciences, Texas Technological College, Lubbock, Texas (U.S.A.)

ELSEVIER PUBLISHING COMPANY Amsterdam London New York 1968

ELSEVIER PUBLISHING COMPANY
335 JAN VAN GALENSTRAAT, P.O. BOX 211, AMSTERDAM, THE NETHERLANDS

ELSEVIER PUBLISHING COMPANY LTD.
BARKING, ESSEX, ENGLAND

AMERICAN ELSEVIER PUBLISHING COMPANY, INC.
52 VANDERBILT AVENUE, NEW YORK, NEW YORK 10017

LIBRARY OF CONGRESS CATALOG CARD NUMBER 68-15623

WITH 125 ILLUSTRATIONS AND 22 TABLES

PRINTED IN THE NETHERLANDS

To and for Rosie

Aerial photograph (view to the south) of the Rio Grande Valley near El Paso, Texas (arrow), and part of north-western Chihuahua, Mexico, showing the southern part of the 10,000 sq. mile basin of pluvial Lake Palomas. Dashed line approximates the U.S.–Mexico border. This is the great basin which received the Pleistocene flow of the Rio Grande River before it established its present course south-east of El Paso sometime after medial Kansan (700,000 years B.P.), but before Bonneville–Lahontan (14,000 years B.P.) time. (Photo by J. A. McDivitt and Ed White, June, 1965, courtesy National Aeronautics and Space Administration.)

PREFACE

My purpose in writing this book (I presuppose most readers will have a rudimentary knowledge of introductory geology, chemistry, and physics) is to illustrate and popularize the study of ancient lake basins, and particularly to emphasize their importance as indicators of paleoclimatology. The need for a text on paleolimnological techniques became apparent several years ago when I began a detailed study of the West Texas pluvial lake basins. This book, mainly the result of lake studies in West Texas and Mexico, is apparently the first to gather and review, in a generalized manner, study methods from various disciplines expressly for the study of ancient lake basins.

Many excellent texts deal with *some* of the various aspects of paleolimnology. J. K. Charlesworth's *The Quaternary Era* (1957) and P. Woldstedt's *Das Eiszeitalter* (1954–1958) concentrate mainly on geological considerations, R. F. Flint's *Glacial and Pleistocene Geology* (1957) on glacial geomorphology, and K. W. Butzer's *Environment and Archaeology* (1964) weaves together Pleistocene environmental and archaeological data, but paleolimnological study is passed over lightly. Even so, the cause, existence, and influence of ancient lakes, particularly those of the glacial or pluvial periods, has been mentioned in various texts on geography, pedology, climatology, archaeology, physical geology, zoology, historical geology, geomorphology, limnology, and hydrology. Therefore, it is expected that the information contained will be of interest to foresters, soil scientists, geographers, zoologists, paleoecologists, as well as to the professional geologist, oceanographer, and archaeologist.

Evidence of ancient or fossil lakes is admittedly often argumentative, hidden from view, or simply unrecognizable; yet this challenge, where all of the professional training of field and office, and of various related subjects, must be utilized, is the very thing which makes the study of paleolimnology one of the most exciting fields of the geosciences. Because of these inherent difficulties, this book is arranged in three main parts; the first dealing with the formation, development, and description of lake basins, the second with lake environments, and the third with paleolake basins and methods of study. Thus the first two parts set the stage for the last section.

The author is, by training and professional experience, a geologist and not a chemist or biologist. Therefore, data concerning the physics, chemistry, and/or biology of lake waters has been synthesized from the works of others, either by review of research reports in professional journals or from appropriate texts. Obviously in any introductory work such as this certain important papers have been omitted because of content or oversight; yet the author emphasizes that omission of any paper in no way reflects personal or professional bias. The references I feel to be particularly important have been included in the text, the great number of which lead, in many places, to an inadvertent staccato style, hopefully balanced in many places by free use of the split infinitive.

I am indebted to the paleolimnological foundations long ago established by G. E. Hutchinson, P. B. Sears, W. H. Bradley, and E. S. Deevey, and to my many colleagues and associates. I particularly thank R. A. Kopp, J. P. Brand, and F. E. Green for early suggestions concerning many of the various phases of the multiple studies this text includes, and I am very grateful to my close associate in lake studies, W. T. Parry, for general review of the entire manuscript. Certainly my sincere appreciation is extended to the many persons who helped secure suitable illustrations, particularly to C. Warren Bonython and R. W. Galloway who supplied valuable data on the Australian basins. J. T. Neal, A. J. Eardley, J. C. Frye, D. W. Scholl, and I. S. Allison along with J. H. Feth, G. I. Smith, C. T. Snyder, and I. P. Shultz of the U.S. Geological Survey, were unduly cooperative.

There is naturally a time when a person is writing a book or not writing a book, but during the latter period I now realize that every investigation or professional field experience in some way relates to the task ahead. The author, therefore, fully realizes the tremendous contributions and sacrifices made by his late wife, Rosemary, toward this end. In the many-sided role of wife, mother, and sweetheart one day and artist, editor, and field assistant another, she provided the stability, peace-of-mind, and particularly encouragement needed for the drudgery of my preliminary studies. Thus, although she only lived to know of the title and review the initial chapters, this book is the direct result of her patience, attitude, and companionship during the formative nine years. Likewise, I would be derelict in not recognizing the many contributions of my present wife whose very presence supplied the encouragement and personal organization needed to finally complete the manuscript.

CONTENTS

INTRODUCTION

Limnology, based on the 1893 definition in the *Geographic Journal*, is "the scientific study of lakes." The first scientific lake study, in about 1869, dealt mainly with physiochemical relations of Lake Geneva, Switzerland. Subsequent studies of lakes in the north–central United States, which concentrated on ecological relations and physiochemistry, were pioneered principally by E. A. Birge and Chancey Juday. However, throughout these nearly 100 years of lake study little attention centered on geological aspects of lake basins, undoubtedly because the water presents a nearly unsurmountable barrier to the geologist attempting to determine origin of the basin and/or stratigraphy of the lake sediments. Consequently, it is not surprising that limnology as a science developed principally due to efforts of biologists and chemists. Once a lake looses its water, the science of *paleolimnology* or "old lake" geology comes into play. Paleolimnology naturally overlaps the realm of the biologist, chemist, and physicist, but is basically and ideally suited to the geologist. Paleolimnology, then, is the recognition and study of ancient lakes, usually by investigation of lacustrine strata and shore features, although considerable emphasis is also placed on paleoclimatic parameters deduced from study of the hydrologic balance of the old lakes. This type of study is in itself somewhat definitive of surrounding geography and geology.

Paleolimnology originated with the 1885 publication of RUSSELL's study of Lake Lahontan and the 1890 treatise of GILBERT's on Pleistocene Lake Bonneville. Russell's and Gilbert's works focused attention on two of the largest Pleistocene pluvial lake basins in the western United States, but is was not until MEINZER (1922) published his map that most geologists realized the great number, extent, and probable geologic importance of the ancient lake basins in the western United States. Pleistocene pluvial lake basins occur throughout the world, and during the last 65 years, many have been studied in great detail. Innumerable Pleistocene (and earlier Tertiary) lake basins are known from parts of the western United States and Mexico, from the northern Sahara, Africa, and from central Australia; and more are being discovered yearly. The study of ancient lake basins, which even now seems to be extending to celestial objects (UREY, 1967), is therefore being used to unlock the secrets of the recent geological past, and particularly to establish the paleoenvironmental conditions of the Pleistocene in many parts of the world.

The 1964 maps of FETH and SNYDER et al. show the great extent of the majority of the Cenozoic lake basins of the western United States. Because of their unusually great size and wide distribution, all geologists should be thoroughly familiar with lacustrine deposits and features, yet no college or university in the United States (known to the author) devotes specialized geologic study, on the undergraduate level, to lake basins. Brief mention of lacustrine morphology may be passed over lightly in geomorphology, but the nearest true courses in lacustrine geology are apparently those offered by biology departments, generally when studying ecology or limnology.

There is also a general absence of texts dealing solely with the science of paleolimnology. HUTCHINSON's *Treatise on Limnology*, vol.1 (1957), although certainly the most detailed book on general limnology, fails to discuss paleolimnological applications, and HUTCHINSON (1967) concentrates on biology.

Fortunately the author does not intend to cover each topic that might somehow be related to ancient lake basins, nor even each topic listed in the index in the fullest detail, for this would not only be repetitious but nearly impossible. Rather, since much of the applicable material is already detailed by chemists, physicists, and biologists, the author presents, in introductory condensed form, those facets of other disciplines which have particular significance to paleolimnological study.

Part I. The Lake Basin

All lakes are transitory in the geologic record because the very nature of the lake basin, a topographic low completely surrounded by higher areas, insures its inevitable destruction. Thus, many lake basins, often during the short life span of a man, pass through a recognizable cycle of destruction, from lake to pond to marsh to swamp to dry land. An exact definition is therefore necessary, because what may be regarded as a lake in one part of the country may be termed a pond, marsh, bog, or swamp in another area.

FOREL (1892) considered any basin with deep water, as long as it was not connected to the sea, a *lake*: if water depth were shallow, the term *pond* was used. MUTTKOWSKI (1918) thought size and depth of the water body distinguished lakes from ponds, but later investigators (CARPENTER, 1928; WELCH, 1952; HUTCHINSON, 1957) more or less utilize FOREL's (1892) classification.

The writer considers a *lake* a body of water which is too deep to permit vegetation[1] to take root completely across the water expanse, whereas a *pond* is a small fresh-water accumulation across which vegetation may or may not be more or less continuous (Fig.1). The terms swamp, marsh, and bog are often considered syno-

Fig.1. Small pond, Marion County, Florida, the shallow depth revealed by the trees. Many parts of the surrounding area are either swampy or marshy. (Photo by J. T. Pardee, courtesy U.S. Geological Survey.)

---

[1] This definition excludes subaqueous vegetation.

nymous in that all refer to areas of poor drainage. However, limnologists consider saturated ground supporting trees a *swamp*; without trees, but with aquatic vegetation and grasses, a *marsh*. The term *bog* refers to any area of saturated ground which contains accumulations of *peat*. Naturally, both the marsh and the swamp may accumulate peat if old enough and in the higher latitudes where peat readily accumulates.

Although lake basins form in response to various geologic reasons, few are preserved or recognized in the geologic column. For instance, in the western United States only two occurrences of Precambrian (LUDLUM, 1942; FENTON and FENTON, 1957) and one occurrence of Permo–Pennsylvanian (HUBERT, 1958) lacustrine strata are known. Several Mesozoic lacustrine occurrences are recognized (FETH, 1964), but by far the greater percentage of recognized ancient lake basins are those of Cenozoic age, and particularly those of Pleistocene age. We do know that during the Tertiary there were many lakes in the intermontane valleys of Utah, Wyoming, Colorado, Nevada, and Idaho (LOVEJOY, 1960, 1962; MORRISON, 1966), but sparse exposures, tectonic disturbances, and the peculiarity of stratigraphic distribution have restricted paleolimnological field study to mainly the Pleistocene lake basins, with several notable exceptions such as the lacustrine deposits of the Green River basin.

The world's lakes, 60% of which are fresh, cover about 1% of the earth's dryland surface. Many occur in recently glaciated (Pleistocene) areas of the Northern Hemisphere, such as Scandinavia (Finland alone has at least 55,000), Canada, and the states of Minnesota ("Land of 10,000 Lakes"), Wisconsin, and Michigan. Alaska has over three million lakes with surface areas over 20 acres!

Lake size is not geographically controlled in that large lakes and/or lake basins, those with surface areas exceeding 200 sq. miles, are not concentrated in any one country or hemisphere. The largest lake in the world, although actually an isolated remnant of the ocean, is the Caspian Sea (163,000–170,000 sq. miles). Excluding the Caspian Sea, the Great Lakes complex of North America, covering about 95,000–127,000 sq. miles, is the largest fresh water system, Lake Superior (31,820 sq. miles) being the largest individual lake. Lake Eyre, South Australia, has one of the largest (500,000 sq. miles) drainage basins in the world (PRICE, 1955), although the present playa only covers about 3,700 sq. miles. Lake Baikal, in eastern Siberia, though only covering about 12,150–13,300 sq. miles, less than half the area of Lake Superior, contains about 5,800 cubic miles of water, more than any other lake in the world and more than all of the Great Lakes combined.

Chapter 1

FORMATION OF LAKE BASINS

No lake has ever existed without a basin or depression in which water accumulated; therefore, study of ancient lakes and ancient lake basins is deeply concerned with origins of the original basins. Classifications for lake basin origins were developed by DAVIS (1882), PENCK (1882), and SUPAN (1896); later workers included DELEBECQUE (1898) and HALBFASS (1923), and more recently ZUMBERGE (1952) and HUTCHINSON (1957).

HUTCHINSON (1957) presents the most complete classification of lake basin origins, listing eleven major processes which produce 75 different types of basins. The major processes of lake basin formation are generally regionally controlled, yet

Fig.2. Searles Lake basin, California, one of a series of four interconnected tectonic basins. Cores, seismic, and gravity indicate at least 3,200 ft. of Cenozoic fill in the basin, 875 ft. of which is known to be lacustrine. Notice high-level abandoned shoreline marked by arrows. (Photo by courtesy of American Potash and Chemical Corporation.)

the exact type of basin and its particular location is often locally determined for each basin by intense local activity. The following is an abbreviated list of the eleven major processes which have been involved in origin of the world's lake basins.

Lake basins of tectonic origin are formed by movements of the earth's crust. The best examples of lake basins of this type, like the Warner Lakes of southern Oregon, Tahoe and other intermontane basins in California (Fig.2), Baikal in Russia, and Tanganyika in Africa, have generally formed in grabens. Tectonic uplift as well as subsidence may be of regional or local extent, but both can produce lake basins. For instance, the regional and local uplifts of the Colorado Plateau produced old Lake Bonneville's basin, but local, gentle uplifts produced the basin of Lake Victoria, Africa, and very local subsidence, caused by the New Madrid earthquake (1811), allowed formation of Reelfoot Lake, Tennessee. Post-Pleistocene movement of the Cullarin Horst, Australia, effectively blocked the Molonglo River drainage producing Burbong-Carwoola Lake (WILSON, 1966), and geophysical studies suggest the escarpment along the west side of Lake George, Australia, is associated with a fault (MANN, 1966). The great size and lacustrine sedimentation in the Lake Dieri Basin, South Australia, also resulted from a regional tectonic downwarp.

Fig.3. Lake San Cristobal, Lake Fork, Gunnison River, Colorado, formed behind the Slumgullion Slide. (Photo by Vincent Kelley.)

Fig.4. Earthquake Lake, Madison River Canyon, Gallatin National Forest, Montana. This basin, formed by the slide of 40,000,000 cubic yards of mainly metamorphic rock triggered by an earthquake the night of August 17, 1959, blocked the Madison River. (Photo by U. R. Stacy, by courtesy of U.S. Geological Survey.)

MASS MOVEMENT BASINS

Steep-walled stream valleys often give rise to landslides which block valley drainage to create a lake. Disastrous floods resulting from the destruction of the incompetent, newly-formed dams often occur, thus the lakes seldom remain long enough to become well known. Lakes San Cristobal in Colorado (Fig.3), Earthquake Lake, Montana (Fig.4), and Gros Ventre in Wyoming (Fig.5) were produced by mass movements blocking valley drainage. Several lake basins in California, such as Broadwell, Troy Dry Lake, Deadman, and Means, formed by alluvial fan damming (STONE, 1956).

VOLCANIC BASINS

Volcanic activity, by several different methods, may form basins which, if in a temperate climate, may contain water. Crater Lake, Oregon (Fig.6), exists in a caldera, and Lake Taupo, New Zealand, and Lake Albano, Italy, are also probable caldera basin lakes. Pluvermaar, Germany, Lake Viti, Iceland, and Zuni Salt Lake, New Mexico (Fig.7), exist in maare; and Lake Texcoco, Mexico, in a depression ringed

Fig.5. Gros Ventre Lake, Wyoming, formed by the Gros Ventre landslide from which picture was taken. (Photo by W. C. Alden, by courtesy U.S. Geological Survey.)

Fig.6. The basin of Crater Lake, Oregon, 6 miles wide and 4,000 ft. deep, is the caldera of extinct volcanic Mt. Mazama. Wizard Island, in the foreground, rises 2,000 ft. from the crater floor and about 700 ft. above lake surface. (Photo by courtesy of Oregon State Highway Department.)

Fig.7. Zuni Salt Lake, New Mexico, contained within a volcanic maar. Notice central cinder cones which form during the final phase of lava extrusion during maar formation. (Photo by M. K. Shaler, by courtesy of U.S. Geological Survey.)

Fig.8. The lava dam holding Snag Lake, Lassen Volcanic National Park, California. (Photo by J. S. Diller, by courtesy of U.S. Geological Survey.)

by massive volcanic mountains. Several lake basins in France (GLANGEAUND, 1913), Africa (WORTHINGTON, 1932), Japan (YOSHIMURA, 1938), and New Zealand (COTTON, 1952) were produced by lava dams. In the United States, Snag Lake, California (Fig.8) is a well-known example of a lake basin produced by blocking of drainage by a lava flow. In Guatemala, Atitlan Lake was formed by a lava dam blocking the flow of two rivers and Lake Van, Turkey, covering 1,453 sq. miles, was formed by a lava dam from the nearby volcano Nimrnd. Perhaps the simplest of the volcanic-related basins are those formed by local collapse or natural irregularities of a lava flow, Yellowstone Lake, Wyoming, being a good example. The hydrothermal explosion basins in Yellowstone Park (MUFFLER et al., 1967) probably also belong in this category.

METEORIC BASINS

Lake basins due to meteoric impact are the rarest type. Meteor Crater, Arizona (Fig.9), once contained a Pleistocene lake but is dry today. The Ungava or Chubb Lake, Ungava, Quebec, Canada (Fig.10), is the best known meteoric lake basin, having a depth of about 720 ft. Also see CASSIDY (1967) on the Campo del Cielo area.

Fig.9. Meteor Crater, Arizona, a basin produced by meteoric impact. Notice small playa in center, all that remains of a larger Pleistocene lake which left some 180 ft. of lacustrine sediment in the basin. (Photo by courtesy of Frontier Airlines.)

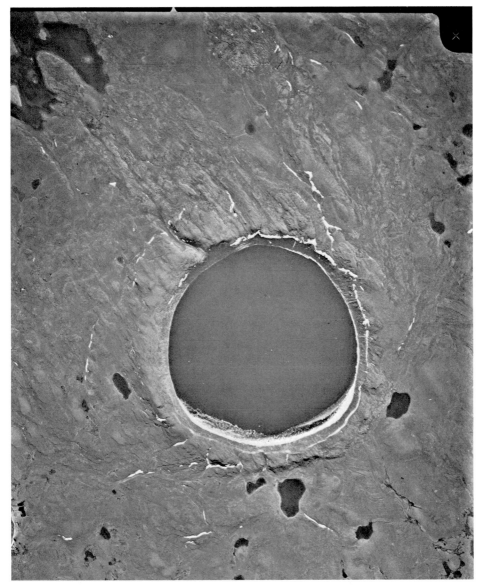

Fig.10. Chubb or Ungava Lake, Quebec, Canada, an almost perfect circular basin. The basin was formed by meteorite impact, today having a diameter of about 2 miles. (Photo by courtesy of Department of Mines and Technical Surveys, National Air Photo Library, Ottawa, Canada.)

SOLUTION BASINS

Lake basins are produced by solution of rock, usually limestone, rock salt, and gypsum (Ft. Bend, Texas), providing the bottoms of the sinks intersect the local water table. Such widespread *karst* areas, which may form very small (Fig.11) or very large

Fig.11. "St. Jacobs Well", Clark County, Kansas. A typical example of a small sink hole lake. (Photo by courtesy of J. C. Frye.)

lake basins, occur in the central United States (Indiana, Kentucky, Tennessee), Florida, the Yucatan Peninsula, Switzerland, in the karst region of the Balkan Peninsula and perhaps in the Cape York Peninsula area, Australia.

GLACIAL BASINS

Glaciation has directly or indirectly formed or caused the development of more lake basins and lakes than all of the other geological processes combined. Glaciers have produced literally millions of tarn or cirque (Fig.12), paternoster (Fig.13), moraine (Fig.14, 15)[1], drift and fjord lakes throughout North America, Europe, and Asia. Indirectly, Pleistocene pluvial climates so increased the water regimen over normally dry desert areas of the western United States, Mexico, Africa, and Asia that all enclosed topographic lows filled with water, some forming lakes covering at least 20,000 sq. miles (Fig.91). Proglacial lakes, those contemporaneous with the ice, are generally short lived and consequently of little paleolimnological importance.

---

[1] There is currently some question as to whether the famous Finger Lakes of New York state actually resulted from pluvial or glacial processes (CLAYTON, 1965; COATES, 1966).

Fig.12. A small tarn or cirque lake, Beartooth Mountains, Montana. (Photo by George Grant, by courtesy of National Park Service.)

Fig.13. Paternoster lakes on the crest between the middle and south branches of South Fork, San Joaquin River, Sierra Nevada, California. (Photo by G. K. Gilbert, by courtesy of U.S. Geological Survey.)

Fig.14. Moraine-dammed lakes on shelf above canyon of South Fork, San Joaquin River, California, (Photo by F. E. Matthes, by courtesy of U.S. Geological Survey.)

Fig.15. Jackson Lake, Wyoming, a basin created by glacial end moraine. (Photo by George Grant, by courtesy of the U.S. Department of Interior, National Park Service.)

FLUVIATILE BASINS

Several different types of lakes are formed by stream action, the most important of which are the oxbow (Fig.16), deltaic, and lateral. During Pleistocene time increased runoff from glacial melt and pluvial rains produced river-gouged depressions, forming lakes in the northern Sahara, the Kalahari, Africa, and on the southern High Plains of West Texas (Fig.17). Lateral lakes, which form in tributary valleys due to flooding by a larger stream whose level has been raised by channel aggradation, are little known but considered by HUTCHINSON (1957) to be most important. Deltaic lakes appear on large river deltas due to shallow basins being formed behind distri-

Fig.16. Lake Lee, Mississippi, an oxbow lake about 10 miles south of Greenville. (Photo by courtesy of U.S. Army Engineer District, Vicksburg, Mississippi.)

Fig.17. Aerial photograph of North T-Bar Lake, Lynn County, Texas, an example of a river-gouge depression. Notice the linear shape and the numerous rain-filled deflation basins in the background. The arrow marks South T-Bar Lake. (Photo by the author.)

butary levees, the best example perhaps being Lake Pontchartrain, Louisiana. The Salton Sea (Fig.18), probably an example of a structural basin, was apparently fed during the Pleistocene by a distributary of the Colorado River; however, today the basin is isolated from the Colorado by old delta deposits.

WIND BASINS

Deflation basins formed by removal of fine-grained clay and sand are produced only in semi-arid to arid areas which have a surplus of fine-grained surface debris and characteristically high winds. Thousands of deflation basins exist on the High Plains of the United States (Fig.19), across the Kalahari of Africa, in Asia, South America, and in central Australia. Wind-blown loess, as on the southern High Plains of West Texas, or wind-blown sand as occurs in many river valleys, also frequently produces lake basins by blocking of local drainage. Moses Lake, Washington (Fig.20), was formed by blocking sand dunes.

ORGANIC BASINS

Small lake basins are frequently formed by thick growths or falls of vegetation as in peat bogs. Such basins are of little importance to paleolimnologists.

ANIMAL BASINS

Lakes formed by mammals such as beaver and/or man are generally unimportant to the geologist, principally because they are extremely small, shallow, transitory, and have no large ancient representation. Future geologists will, of course, find evidence of the existence of lakes like Meade, Norris, or Texoma, but future problems can not be here anticipated.

In many parts of the world, basins have been ascribed to various local animals;

Fig.18. Aerial photograph of the Salton Sea, California, showing isolation by delta deposits from present course of the Colorado River to the far right. The water in the Salton Sea accumulated by inadvertent flooding from the Colorado River from 1905 to 1907. About 450 sq. miles of the basin was flooded to a depth of 93 ft. Today evaporation is causing rapid desiccation of the lake. (Photo by Majors J. A. McDivitt and E. White, June, 1965, by courtesy of National Aeronautics and Space Administration.)

Fig.19. Typical deflation basins, southern High Plains, West Texas. Notice the large mud cracks and salt-rimming in the nearest basin. (Photo by the author.)

Fig.20. Moses Lake, Washington, formed in a basin created by sand dunes (foreground) blocking drainage of Rocky Ford Creek. (Photo by E. Hertzog, by courtesy of Bureau of Reclamation.)

Fig.21. Small lake basin, Lynn County, Texas, that was probably initiated by cattle and which has been continually enlarged by wind deflation and animal pawing. (Photo by the author.)

Fig.22. The Texas Gulf Coast, Jefferson County, 4 miles south of Sabine Pass, view to the north. Shaping of some basins due to wind and resultant end current erosion probably produces the oval or elliptical form. (Photo by courtesy of D. E. Feray.)

perhaps the best known being the so-called "buffalo wallows" of the southern High Plains of West Texas and eastern New Mexico. Wild and even domestic animals now accentuate local topographic lows when searching for water, cool mud, and precipitated salts (Fig.21), thus the vast extinct herds that once roamed the various steppes of the world may have produced more basins than are presently realized. Present animal wallows are always small (8–10 ft. in diameter) and shallow (1–2 ft.): older "buffalo wallows" were reported (CUSTER, 1874) about the same size.

SHORELINE BASINS

Most lakes associated with shorelines, either oceanic or lacustrine, are primarily the result of depositional rather than erosional processes, although many coastal basins are shaped by the wind (end-current erosion), taking a typical oval or elliptical shape (Fig.22). Linear lakes (Fig.23) are also quite common, the basins generally confined to depressions between bars of prograding shorelines. Oceanic coastal lakes in the Cape Cod area or along the Gulf Coast have been produced by

Fig.23. North of Bayou Moreau, Louisiana, 50 miles south of New Orleans, view to the southwest. Linear basins formed by depressions between bars on a chenier plain or a prograding shoreline. (Photo by courtesy of D. E. Feray.)

Fig.24. Bay Marchand, east of Belle Pass of Bayou Lafourche, Louisiana, 50 miles south of New Orleans, view to the north. Salinity of such Recent, near-ocean lakes, formed by deposition of bars, ranges from brackish to nearly fresh. (Photo by courtesy of D. E. Feray.)

deposition of bars (Fig.24), similar deposition often dividing large lakes into smaller lakes.

One unusual type of shoreline basin is that of Lake Malar, Sweden (440 sq. miles). Many thousands of years ago the present Lake Malar area was a bay of the Baltic Sea, but isostatic rebound due to removal of Pleistocene ice cut off the bay from the sea about 770 years ago.

It is unusual to find only one lake in an area because a principal process of lake formation invariably affects a broad geographic region. In fact, of the eleven major geologic processes responsible for the formation of the world's lake basins, only one, meteoric impact, exists on a local restricted scale. An explanation for the origin of any lake basin may then often be gained simply by a knowledge of local regional geology, although the possibility of complicating factors, which are usually alarmingly obvious, must always be weighed. For instance, Odessa Crater, Texas, is in a semi-desert area characterized by deflation basins, yet its meteoric origin is quite clear to all geologists. However, the famous Afton Craters (Kilburn and Hunts Holes) of southern New Mexico (Fig.25), because of a superficial resemblance to Meteor Crater, Arizona (Fig.9), perplexed geologists for years (LEE, 1907; DARTON, 1916;

Fig.25. Kilborne Maar (Hole), New Mexico. Notice resemblance to Meteor Crater, Arizona (Fig.9), but the absence of central cinder cones as at Zuni Salt Lake (Fig.7). The central playa is a remnant of a much larger playa formed on an unknown thickness of Pleistocene lacustrine fill. (Photo by the author.)

REICHE, 1940). Recent work (SHOEMAKER, 1962; REEVES and DE HON, 1965; DE HON and REEVES, 1966) definitely shows the volcanic origin of the Afton Craters, yet local ranchers and most visitors still consider them meteoric craters!

Certainly throughout the world there are lake basins whose origins do not correspond to any of the preceding, and there are basins where a particular origin could overlap into different categories. The cave-in lake basins (thermokarst) of eastern Alaska (WALLACE, 1948), produced by permafrost thawing and consequent surficial settling to form a shallow basin, might be placed in the structural category, but the slight contraction of the fine-grained surface debris hardly seems of the proper magnitude. Melting of the permafrost may also suggest a solution basin, thus the term "thermokarst", but actually no rock or soil is removed, only soil moisture. Cave-in basins then, along with geyser basins (solutional?, structural?) as along the Rio Salado, New Mexico or in Warm Spring Canyon, Wyoming, may best be classified as miscellaneous.

Chapter 2

QUANTITATIVE DESCRIPTION OF LAKE BASINS

Several quantitative parameters and their definitions are used by limnologists for describing a lake. Only the following are useful when working with ancient lake basins.

LENGTH AND WIDTH

The length and width of a lake basin (or lake) are measured from shore to shore at right angles to one another, the length being the greater distance. Units may be in feet or miles.

VOLUME AND AREA

The volume of a lake basin may be determined by evelation of the HUTCHINSON (1957) integral:

$$V = \int_{Z=0}^{Z=Z_M} A_z \cdot d_z$$

or by $V = h/3(A_1 + A_2 + \sqrt{A_1 A_2})$ where A_1 and A_2 refer to the upper and lower surfaces respectively of some contour stratum, h representing the contour stratum height. The area of the lake basin (A) or of any contour stratum Z is best determined by planimetry.

MAXIMUM AND MEAN DEPTH

The maximum depth of a lake depends on depth of the basin, amount of water in the lake, and amount of sedimentation in the basin; thus depth is subject to rapid change. The mean depth is determined by dividing the volume of a lake by its area.

LENGTH AND DEVELOPMENT OF SHORELINE

The length of a lake's shoreline is easily measured by a chartometer on any topographic map of suitable scale. The shoreline development (SD) is merely a quantitative description of the length of the shoreline (SL) to the length of the circum-

Fig.26. Aerial photograph of Buffalo Lake, Texas, view to the southeast. Notice extreme length of shoreline and consequently high shoreline development (*SD*) resulting from damming of Yellowhouse Canyon to form the spring-fed basin. (Photo by the author.)

ference of a circle whose area is equal to that of the lake. This may be expressed as:

$$SD = \frac{SL}{2\sqrt{\pi A}}$$

The shoreline development for a circular lake, such as Ungava (Fig.10), is very near unity, but for basins like Buffalo Lake, Texas (Fig.26), formed by damming of a canyon, or for basins formed by grabens or fjords, the shoreline development may exceed 4 or 5.

ELLIPTICITY

The ellipticity (*E*) of a lake or lake basin is given by the length (*L*) minus the width (*W*) divided by the length, or:

$$E = \frac{L-W}{L}$$

Paleolimnologists seldom use extensive quantitative descriptions for ancient lakes and basins, thus those interested in detailed lake morphometry are referred to HUTCHINSON (1957). Length, width, maximum depth, and length of shoreline may be quoted and, when comparing the origin of one lake basin to the genesis of other lake basins, the shoreline development and ellipticity may be useful (REEVES, 1966).

Chapter 3

SHAPE AND DEVELOPMENT OF LAKE BASINS

A lake basin may be classified by reference to its geometric shape which, incidentally, generally results from mode of origin. The most common lake basins according to shape are:

(*1*) *Circular basins*—the shoreline is nearly equal in length to the length of a circle of equal area to that of the lake; development nears unity. Caldera lakes, maare, meteorite craters, sink holes, and blowouts are characteristic of this type, Chubb or Ungava Lake, Quebec, Canada, being one of the most perfect examples (Fig.10).

(*2*) *Subcircular basins*—the shoreline development of subcircular basins is farther from unity than for circular basins in that the shoreline becomes longer as ellipticity increases. The typical kidney-shape of tarns is a good example.

(*3*) *Elliptical basins*—shoreline development even farther from unity than for subcircular basins, with basin length generally twice the width. Best examples are the oriented lake basins of the Arctic or the Carolina "bays" (Fig.27).

(*4*) *Lunate basins*—typified by oxbow lakes where basin length is many times basin width (Fig.16).

(*5*) *Subrectangular basins*—basins whose length/width ratio is several times greater than that of lunate basins. The "Finger Lakes" of upper New York, prograding shoreline basins, or basins created by structural or glacial control are good examples.

(*6*) *Dendritic basins*—produced by the flooding of a stream valley system, usually by formation of a dam, natural or otherwise.

(*7*) *Triangular basins*—generally produced by flooding behind coastal bars (Fig.22).

(*8*) *Irregular basins*—any lake basin that cannot readily fit previous listed categories, usually produced by interference or joining of several basins or by glacial scouring of complicated or structurally disturbed strata. The very irregular shape of the Lake Palomas, Mexico, basin is shown by the Frontispiece. Basin configuration is the result of faulting, volcanic action, tectonic uplifts, and deflation.

No lake basin is ever in equilibrium with its surrounding drainage basin, thus continual modification by erosion or deposition takes place whether the basin contains water or not. The shoreline undergoes change due to the work of waves and currents, the end result being a gently sloping terrace known as the *beach* (Fig.28) above water and the *littoral shelf* or *shore terrace* immediately offshore, the littoral shelf often being exposed by low or total absence of water (Fig.29). The landward edge of the beach is marked by a *wave-cut cliff* which may have a wave-cut groove at its base (Fig.30). The height of the wave-cut cliff depends on innumerable vari-

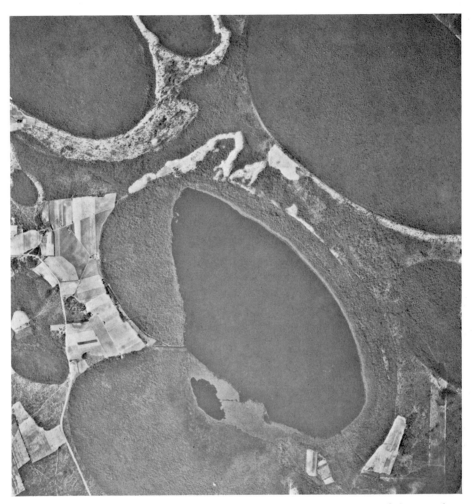

Fig.27. The Carolina "bays" in Bladen County, North Carolina. Thousands of these northwest–southeast oriented basins occur along the Atlantic coastal strip of Georgia, South Carolina, and North Carolina. Notice oval shape, intersection and partial filling. (Photo by courtesy of the U.S. Department of Agriculture.)

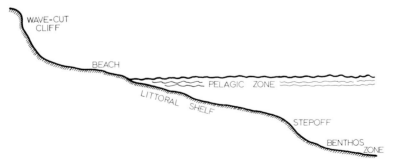

Fig.28. Generalized cross-section of a lake and associated shore.

Fig.29. Shoreline of Lake Eyre, South Australia, showing the rippled sand beach of Sulphur Peninsula and littoral shelf exposed by absence of water and the adjacent wave-cut cliff. (Photo by courtesy of C. Warren Bonython.)

ables, the most important of which are relief, lake and wave size, lithology, and local environment. Wave-cut cliffs along the West Texas pluvial lakes range from 1 to 3 and up to 10 ft. high, but those along the Norwegian fjord lakes are several hundred feet high. The lake edge of the littoral shelf is often colloquially known as the "*stepoff*"; the open water part of the lake is the *pelagic zone*, and the area of bottom deposition is the *benthos zone*. Fig.28 illustrates these relations.

Water movements due to external causes, usually the wind, are known as currents and are, of course, responsible for most of the secondary shaping of the lake basin; thus, wind is the most important agent affecting the shape of both dry and wet lake basins. The destructiveness of waves, due primarily to the great density

Fig.30. Wave-cut groove and cliff produced by Pleistocene Fort Rock Lake on Fort Rock butte, Lake County, Oregon. Stratification occurs in volcanic breccia. (Photo by I. S. Allison, by courtesy of Oregon State University Press.)

of water, is more or less proportional to wave size. STEVENSON (1852) long ago suggested that wave size was proportional to the square root of the fetch. CORNISH (1934) gives the formula:

$$WH = {}^1/_3 \; F$$

(where WH equals wave height and F equals the fetch) to express wave height. This seems particularly adaptable for small water bodies. SVERDRUP and MUNK (1947) find that wave height (WH) depends only on wind speed and acceleration due to gravity, the relation being:

$$WH = \frac{0.26 \; w^2}{g}$$

Depth of a lake apparently does not affect wave size in small basins, but wave size certainly increases with depth in large lakes (HUTCHINSON, 1957). THIJSSE (1952) finds a definite relation between fetch and depth to develop maximum wave size for any given wind velocity.

Waves breaking obliquely onshore create *longshore currents* which transport near-shore debris eroded and disturbed by wave action to quieter localities along or slightly offshore where deposition as *bars* and *spits* takes place (see Chapter 8). The waves thus contemporaneously act both as an agent of erosion and deposition.

Water movement due to wind is basically different in extremely shallow, shallow to moderate, and deep lakes. In the extremely shallow lakes (depths of only a few inches), as the salt playas of West Texas, Africa, or Australia, the water, when present, may be blown from one end of the playa to the other during wind shifts, always resting in the downwind end. Such surface water movements may take place on a playa several miles long in a period of only one or two hours. In shallow to moderate depth lakes (depths of only a few feet), wind-driven water piles[1] against the lee shore, returning by rip currents (end-currents) formed normal to the wind direction and directed toward the ends of the lake basin (Fig.31). In deep-water lakes subsurface currents develop, more or less parallel to wind direction, their efficiency dependent on existence and/or depth of the submarine density barrier between the warm surface water and colder, deeper water at depth. Unfortunately the erosive effects of such undertow currents are unknown.

LIVINGSTON (1954) first illustrated the principal of end-current erosion as produced by longshore currents in the oriented lakes of northern Alaska, but the most exacting explanation is given by REX (1961). End-current erosion results from a strong, steady wind blowing across a shallow circular lake to produce a pair of gyrating surface currents normal to the wind (Fig.31). The ends of the circular to

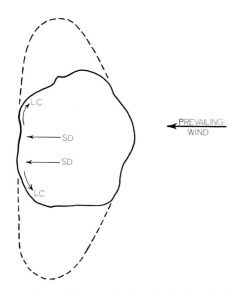

Fig.31. Aerial view of a hypothetical lake basin illustrating the development of end-currents. *SD* = surface drift, *LC* = longshore currents (the end-currents) directed to the ends of the lake which they continually eroded.

----

[1] BONYTHON (1955) recorded at least a 2-ft. piling of water in Lake Eyre, South Australia, due to storm winds.

subcircular lake basin are rapidly eroded by the currents because velocity is at a maximum in the lake ends, thus the basin elongates perpendicular to the prevailing wind, having a near-straight lee shore and a somewhat more irregular windward shore.

Wind produces deflation basins in semi-arid to arid areas which now periodically fill with water during wet seasons. However, during Pleistocene pluvial times wind-excavated basins existed as permanent lakes. Wind-excavated basins tend to elongate parallel to the predominant or prevailing wind, the deflated debris forming dunes at the lee end of the basin (Fig.32). Deflation basins formed by variable winds are more or less circular and surrounded by a smaller, more continuous dune rim of deflated debris.

Lake basins often owe their original shape to a particular genesis, their present configuration or the shape of their interior playa (if dry) resulting from more recent developmental processes. For instance, most of the large pluvial lake basins of the southern High Plains of West Texas are elongate because of a peculiar combination of pluvial stream action, local stratigraphy, and end-current erosion (REEVES, 1966); yet present playas, although obviously resulting from deflation, trend normal to prevailing deflationary winds, the downwind shore being extremely straight. Thus the playas apparently developed their present shapes due to end-current erosion when wet rather than simply in response to the dry deflationary winds. The present playas formed from the ever-present strong to moderate prairie winds. These winds willowed the finest of the fine-grained lacustrine strata exposed in the dry lake beds

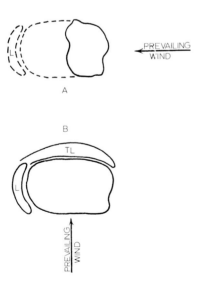

Fig.32. Aerial view of a hypothetical lake showing first, enlargement and alignment with the prevailing wind when dry, deflation producing the lunette (L) on its west side. An environmental change causes a 90° shift in prevailing wind direction plus the filling of the basin with water. Under these conditions the basin aligns perpendicular to the prevailing wind because of end-current erosion, lunette (TL) forming during dry periods.

Fig.33. Large transverse dune parallel to the playa of Yellow Lake, Hockley County, Texas. This dune formed by deflation of fine-grained lacustrine debris < 14,000 years B. P., and probably during the Early Altithermal period. The light colored dunes immediately next to the now dry playa represent Recent winds. Notice the old shoreline in the background (arrows) and the probable deflation basin formed on the old high level lake sediments. (Photo by the author.)

Fig.34. Deflation of south T-Bar playa, Lynn County, Texas, by strong southwesterly winds. Notice high transverse dunes in background. (Photo by the author.)

to produce the massive transverse dunes now bordering their southeastern flanks (Fig.33). Naturally strong winds blowing across dry lake playas will cause deflation, of the fine-grained lacustrine debris (Fig.34), regardless of shape or origin of the lake basin; thus the presence of dunes fringing a playa or basin does not automatically indicate a deflationary origin.

Currents are created, primarily in large lakes, by influents, either because of the volume of water or the density difference caused by temperature, load, or a combination of both. If the density of the influent's water is less than that of the lake's water, a surface flow exists. Subsurface flows are created when influent density is greater than lake density, the turbidity current caused by the silt-laden waters of Lake Meade, Arizona–Nevada, being an appropriate example. Naturally both types of flow cease when equilibrium is established.

Waves rapidly cut a terrace on shores and/or promontories directly facing prevailing winds, often backed by a sharp wave-cut cliff. The debris in some cases may be removed, but is generally deposited on the nearby littoral shelf.

When the majority of lakes or basins in a region exhibit the consequences of a predominant developmental factor, the basins are oriented (Fig.27), the best known examples being the Carolina "bays" (JOHNSON, 1942; COOKE, 1954), the Mackenzie delta, Canada (MACKAY, 1956, 1963), Beni Basin (PLAFKA, 1964), and Alaskan tundra lakes (CARSON and HUSSEY, 1960, 1962) and the basins of the southern High Plains, Texas (REEVES, 1966). Oriented lakes in general are thoroughly discussed by PRICE (1967).

Oriented lakes and basins occur on several different continents under varying climatic environments, yet common to all areas has been the presence of strong prevailing winds. Wind is therefore the critical factor for basin orientation (PRICE, 1967).

REFERENCES

BONYTHON, C. W., 1955. The evaporation rate. In: *Lake Eyre, South Australia, the Great Flooding of 1949–1950.* Roy. Geograph. Soc. Australasia, S. Austr. Branch, Adelaide, S. Austr., pp. 37–56.
BUTZER, K. W., 1964. *Environment and Archaeology, an Introduction to Pleistocene Geography.* Aldine Publ., Co., Chicago, Ill., 525 pp.

CARPENTER, K. E., 1928. *Life in Inland Waters.* Sedgwick and Jackson, New York, N.Y., 267 pp.
CARSON, C. E. and HUSSEY, K. M., 1960. Hydrodynamics in three arctic lakes. *J, Geol.,* 68: 585–600.
CARSON, C. E. and HUSSEY, K. M., 1962. The oriented lakes of arctic Alaska. *J. Geol.,* 70: 417–439.
CASSIDY, W. A., 1967. Meteorite field studies at Campo del Cielo. *Sky Telescope,* 34: 1–8.
CHARLESWORTH, J. K., 1957. *The Quaternary Era.* Arnold, London, 1700 pp.
CLAYTON, K. M., 1965. Glacial erosion in the Finger Lakes region, New York. *Z. Geomorphol.,* 9: 50–62.
COATES, D. R., 1966. Discussion of K. M. Clayton "Glacial erosion in the Finger Lakes region, New York". *Z. Geomorphol.,* 10: 469–474.
COOKE, C. W., 1954. Carolina bays and the shapes of eddies. *U.S. Geol. Surv., Profess. Papers,* 245–I: 195–207.
CORNISH, V., 1934. Ocean waves and kindred geophysical phenomena and additional notes by Harold Jeffreys. *Camb. Univ. Press, Publ.,* 15: 164 pp.
COTTON, C. A., 1952. *Geomorphology.* Whitcombe and Tombs, Christchurch, 505 pp.
CUSTER, G. A., 1874. *My Life on the Plains or Personal Experiences with Indians.* Sheldon, New York, N.Y., 256 pp.

DARTON, N. H., 1916. Explosion craters. *Sci. Monthly,* 3: 417–430.
DAVIS, W. M., 1882. On the classification of lake basins. *Proc., Boston Soc. Nat. History,* 21: 315–381.
DELEBECQUE, A., 1898. *Les Lacs Français.* Chamerot et Renouard, Paris, 436 pp.
DE HON, R. A. and REEVES JR., C. C., 1966. A maar origin for Hunt's Hole, Dona Ana County, New Mexico. *Texas J. Sci.,* 18: 296–316.

FENTON, C. L. and FENTON, M. A., 1957. Paleoecology of the Precambrian of northwestern North America. In: *Treatise on Name Ecology and Paleoecology, 2 of Paleoecology—Geol. Soc. Am., Mem.,* 67: 103–116.
FETH, J. H., 1964. Review and annotated bibliography of ancient lake deposits (Precambrian to Pleistocene) in the western United States. *U.S. Geol. Surv., Bull.,* 1080: 119 pp.
FLINT, R. F., 1957. *Glacial and Pleistocene Geology.* Wiley, New York, N.Y., 553 pp.
FOREL, F. A., 1892. *Le Léman: Monographie limnologique, 1. Géographie, Hydrographie, Géologie, Climatologie, Hydrologie.* Rouge, Lausanne, 543 pp.

GILBERT, G. K., 1890. Lake Bonneville. *U.S., Geol. Surv., Monograph,* 1: 438 pp.
GLANGEAUD, P., 1913. Les régions volcaniques du Puy-de-Dôme, 2. La chaîne des Puys. *Bull. Carte Géol., France,* 135.

HALBFASS, W., 1923. *Grundzüge einer vergleichenden Seenkunde.* Borntraeger, Berlin, 354 S.
HUBERT, J. E., 1958. Petrology of the Fountain Formation along the foothills of the Colorado Front Range. *Bull. Geol. Soc. Am.,* 69: 1590 (abstract).
HUTCHINSON, G. E., 1957. *A Treatise on Limnology.* Wiley, New York, N.Y., 1: 1015 pp.
HUTCHINSON, G. E., 1967. *A Treatise on Limnology.* Wiley, New York, N.Y., 2: 1115 pp.

JOHNSON, D. W., 1942. *The Origin of the Carolina Bays*. Columbia Univ. Press, New York, N.Y., 341 pp.

LEE, W. T., 1907. Afton Craters of southern New Mexico. *Bull. Geol. Soc. Am.*, 18: 211–220.
LIVINGSTONE, D. A., 1954. On the orientation of lake basins. *Am. J. Sci.*, 252: 547–554.
LOVEJOY, E. M. P., 1960. Structural implications of the shore lines of the Mio-Pliocene Lake Nevada. *Bull. Geol. Soc. Am.*, 71: 1919.
LOVEJOY, E. M. P., 1962. Mio-Pliocene Lake Nevada. *Geol. Soc. Am., Spec. Papers*, 68: 39 pp.
LUDLUM, J. C., 1942. Precambrian formations at Pocatello, Idaho. *J. Geol.*, 50: 85–95.

MACKAY, J. R., 1956. Notes on oriented lakes of the Liverpool Bay area, Northwest Territories. *Rev. Can. Geol.*, 10: 169–173.
MACKAY, J. R., 1963. The MacKenzie delta area, Northwest Territories, Canada. *Can., Dept. Mines Tech. Surv., Geograph. Branch, Mem.*, 8: 202 pp.
MANN, P., 1966. Geophysical investigation of Lake George. In: *Summary of Symposium on Lake George—Geol. Soc. Australia*, 3.
MEINZER, O. E., 1922. Map of the Pleistocene lakes of the basin-and-range province and its significance. *Bull. Geol. Soc. Am.*, 33: 541–552.
MORRISON, R. B., 1966. Predecessors of Great Salt Lake. In: *Guidebook to the Geology of Utah, 20. The Great Salt Lake*. Utah, Geol. Surv., Salt Lake City, Utah, pp. 77–104.
MUFFLER, L. J. P., WHITE, D. E., TRUESDELL, A. H. and FOURNIER, R. O., 1967. Violent Late Pleistocene hydrothermal explosions in Yellowstone National Park. *Geol. Soc. Am., Ann. Meeting, Program*, 1967: 158.
MUTTKOWSKI, R. A., 1918. The fauna of Lake Mendota — a qualitative and quantitative survey with special reference to the insects. *Trans. Wisconsin Acad. Sci.*, 19: 374–484.

PENCK, A., 1882. *Die Vergletscherung der Deutschen Alpen, ihre Ursachen, Periodische Wiederkehr und ihr Einfluss auf die Bodengestaltung*. Barth, Leipzig, 483 S.
PLAFKA, G., 1964. Oriented lakes and lineaments of North-eastern Bolivia. *Bull. Geol. Soc. Am.*, 75: 503–522.
PRICE, A. G., 1955. Introduction. In: *Lake Eyre, South Australia, The Great Flooding 1949–1950*. Roy. Geograph. Soc. Australasia, S. Austr. Branch, Adelaide, S. Austr.
PRICE, W. A., 1967. Oriented lakes. In: R. W. FAIRBRIDGE (Editor), *Encyclopedia of Earth Sciences*. Reinhold, New York, N.Y., in press.
REEVES JR., C. C., 1966. Pluvial lake basins of West Texas. *J. Geol.*, 74: 269–291.
REEVES JR., C. C. and DE HON, R. A., 1965. Geology of Potrillo Maar, New Mexico and northern Chihuahua, Mexico. *Am. J. Sci.*, 263: 401–409.
REICHE, P., 1940. The origin of Kilbourne Hole, New Mexico. *Am. J. Sci.*, 238: 212–225.
REX, R. W., 1961. Hydrodynamic analysis of circulation and orientation of lakes in Northern Alaska. In: *Geology of the Arctic, II—Proceedings of 1st International Symposium on Arctic Geology*. Univ. Toronto Press, Toronto, Ont., pp. 1021–1043.
RUSSELL, I. C., 1885. Geological history of Lake Lahontan, a Quaternary lake of Northwestern Nevada. *U.S., Geol. Surv., Monograph*, 11: 287 pp.

SHOEMAKER, E. M., 1962. Interpretation of lunar craters. In: Z. KOPAL (Editor), *Physics and Astronomy of the Moon*. Acad. Press, New York, N.Y., 538 pp.
SNYDER, C. T., HARDMAN, G. and ZDENEK, F. F., 1964. Pleistocene lakes in the Great Basin. *U.S., Geol. Surv., Misc. Geol. Invest.*, Map 1–416.
STEVENSON, T., 1852. Observations on the relation between the height of waves and their distance from the windward shore. *Edinburgh, New Jameson's Phil. J.*, 53: 358–359.
STONE, R. O., 1956. *A Geologic Investigation of Playa Lakes*. Thesis, Univ. Southern Calif., Los Angeles, Calif., 302 pp.
SUPAN, A. G., 1896. *Grundzüge der physischen Erdkunde*. 2 Aufl., Leipzig, 706 S.
SVERDRUP, H. M. and MUNK, W. H., 1947. Wind, sea, and swell: Theory of relations for forecasting. *U.S. Navy Dept. Hydrograph. Office Publ.*, 601 (*U.S. Hydrograph. Office Tech. Rept.*, 1): 44 pp.

THIJSSE, J. TH., 1952. Growth of wind-generated waves and energy transfer. In: *Gravity Waves—U.S. Bur. Standards Circ.*, 521: 281–287.

UREY, H., 1967. Water on the moon? *Time*, 89: 46.

WALLACE, R. E., 1948. Cave-in lakes in the Nabesna, Chisana and Tanana River valleys, eastern Alaska. *J. Geol.*, 56: 171–181.
WELCH, P. S., 1952. *Limnology.* McGraw-Hill, New York, N.Y., 538 pp.
WILSON, E. G., 1966. Molonglo River–Lake George Association. In: *Summary of Symposium of Lake George—Geol. Soc. Australia*, 3.
WOLDSTEDT, P., 1954. *Das Eiszeitalter. 1. Die allgemeinen Erscheinungen des Eiszeitalters.* Enke, Stuttgart, 374 S.
WOLDSTEDT, P., 1958. *Das Eiszeitalter. 2. Europa, Vorderasien und Nordafrika in Eiszeitalter.* Enke, Stuttgart, 374 S.
WORTHINGTON, E. B., 1932. The lakes of Kenya and Uganda. *Geograph. J.*, 79: 275–295.

YOSHIMURA, S., 1938. Dissolved oxygen of the lake waters of Japan. *Sci. Rept. Tokyo Bunrika Daigaru Sect. C.*, 8: 63–277.

ZUMBERGE, J. H., 1952. The lakes of Minnesota, their origin and classification. *Bull. Minn. Geol. Surv.*, 35: 99 pp.

Part II. The Lake

The paleolimnologist, scrambling over the bottom of a long extinct lake, unfortunately must work with features altered by weathering, the degree of destruction depending on the age of the basin, competence of the local lacustrine strata, and present and past environmental parameters. An adequate introductory knowledge of physical and chemical limnology or, in other words, of the environment of a lake basin when full of water, is not only invaluable but necessary for accurate interpretation of paleolake features. Obviously, the best understanding of ancient lakes and basins is based on a thorough knowledge of present lakes and their basins. Thus, although water is certainly of primary interest to the limnologist, it is of secondary interest to the paleolimnologist, but perhaps with an importance inversely proportional to its position of interest.

Chapter 4

THE LACUSTRINE ENVIRONMENT

WATER

The science of paleolimnology exists primarily because lake basins have, through various reasons, lost their water. Thus, in attempting to understand evolution or chronology of lake basin history we must first of all be cognizant of the physical environment which existed within the basin during the period of water occupancy.

The chemical formula for water, H_2O, is learned during the early school years, but most students fail to accumulate either the interest or chemistry to thoroughly understand our most important compound. The water molecule forms by covalent bonding of two hydrogen atoms to the single oxygen atom, the water molecules tending to associate by hydrogen bridges (a hydrogen atom between two oxygen atoms) producing an ordered tetrahedral lattice. Seldom, though, is water such a simple compound of hydrogen (^1H) and oxygen (^{16}O) because of the readily available hydrogen isotopes *deuterium* (^2H) and radioactive *tritium* (^3H). Deuterium forms by the addition of one neutron to the hydrogen nucleus, tritium being formed by cosmic radiation ($^{14}N + N \rightarrow {}^{12}C + {}^3H$); however, the low 12½ year half-life of tritium precludes high concentrations in the hydrosphere. Oxygen (^{16}O) may be frequently supplanted by the heavier isotopes ^{17}O and ^{18}O, but studies indicate ^{18}O concentration is greater than ^{17}O but of course less than ^{16}O.

The first physical peculiarity of water is that it is an inorganic liquid occurring at surface pressure and temperatures, a distinction shared only with mercury and perhaps CO_2 contained in pressurized cavities (HAWES, 1881; WRIGHT, 1881). Secondly, water's freezing and boiling points should be about $-150\,°C$ and $-100\,°C$, respectively, alternation to $0\,°C$ and $100\,°C$ caused by polymerization (RANKAMA and SAHAMA, 1950). Physical properties of water that are of importance to paleolimnologists are specific heat, heat of vaporization, density, and solvency.

Surely the most important physical property of water is its ability to absorb and hold heat with little temperature change. This, the *specific heat* of water, means that temperature changes proceed not only at a much slower rate in water, but over a much narrower range when contrasted with the atmosphere. Although it takes a large amount of heat during the early summer to increase the water temperature of a lake, it correspondingly takes a long time to cool the lake during the fall months (Fig.35). This peculiarity is well illustrated by the normal daily minimum temperature being at least $10\,°F$ higher during January and July over the Great Salt Lake, Utah, than over surrounding areas, and by ocean currents, like the Gulf Stream or the

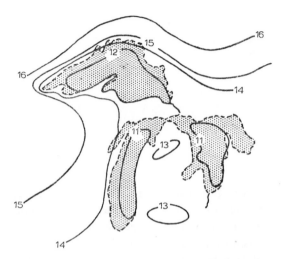

Fig.35. The difference between mean temperature of October and November in °F in the Great Lakes area. The slower advance of cool temperatures over the water areas of Lakes Superior, Michigan, and Huron, is obvious. (Modified after LEIGHLY, 1942.)

Japanese Current, which are able to migrate thousands of miles before they lose identity and effectiveness.

Somewhat related to the specific heat of water is its *latent heat of fusion*, the amount of heat absorbed or produced by the change of ice to water or water to ice *without* a temperature change. The latent heat of fusion for water is eighty times its specific heat, a peculiarity exceeded only by a few elements. This means the larger the body of water, the greater the amount of heat necessary to melt its ice during the

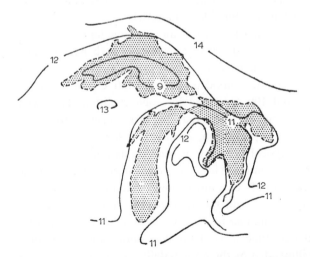

Fig.36. The difference between the mean temperature of April and May in °F in the Great Lakes area. Notice how the water mass of Lake Superior heats much slower than the northern part of southern Michigan. (Modified after LEIGHLY, 1942.)

early spring and consequently the longer to freeze its water during the early fall. However, distribution of surface heat throughout a large lake depends on the wind and extent of fetch; thus in general, the larger the lake, the higher the wind, and the larger the fetch, the more widespread the distribution of heat. The heat stored by a very large lake then greatly affects the temperature march in the area immediately surrounding the lake, the effect more or less being proportional to the lake size. For instance, the mean December air temperature over the Lake Baikal, Russia, area is at least 14 °C warmer than in parts of the immediately surrounding area (HUT-CHINSON, 1957). The same effect exists in the area of the Great Lakes, the most extra-ordinary influence being the long tongue of Lake Michigan and the great expanse of Lake Superior (Fig.35). The reverse is, of course, true as the temperatures start to rise during the spring and summer months. The cold water of the large lake tends to moderate the rate of temperature rise (Fig.36).

Evaporation (vaporization) of water is accomplished only by an inordinate amount of energy which is needed to overcome the hydrogen bonds. Because so much energy is needed, the evaporation rate of water is very low when compared to the evaporation rates of other liquids.

The solvency of water is important to the paleolimnologist because of the chemical precipitates commonly found in ancient lake basins. Although known as the "universal solvent" only about half the naturally occurring elements have been reported from water, yet, the presence of others is suspected. The peculiar molecular arrangement of the hydrogen and oxygen allows a high solvency rate, some compounds (chloride and potassium salts) held in solution by separation of atomic charges, some (ammonia, alcohol, sugar, and organic derivatives) held by atomic bonding, and some by ionization ($C^{2+} + O_2^{2-} + H_2^+ + O^{2-} \rightleftharpoons H_2CO_3$).

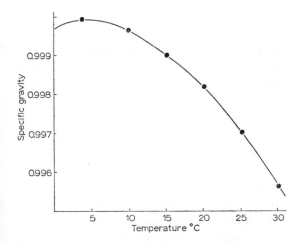

Fig.37. Density and temperature of pure water at sea level. Notice that maximum density occurs at about 4 °C, the water becoming lighter as it heats or cools. At 0 °C the density of water is about 0.999, but ice, at the same temperature, has a density of about 0.917.

Density of pure water is 62.4 lb./cubic ft. with a specific gravity of 1.0 at 3.94 °C, falling to about 0.99 at 0 °C (0.92 for ice at 0 °C); however, to generalize, density increases as temperature decreases, the maximum of 1.0 being reached slightly above freezing (Fig.37). Because dissolved salts, organic debris, silt, and clay increase the density of water, lake waters are often significantly heavier than would be expected at prevailing temperature and pressure.

Although water is, for practical purposes, incompressible, its compressibility does increase with contamination and density. Compressibility depends on water pressure, and would therefore be expected to be much greater in deep ocean trenches than in shallow lakes; however, the difference between shallow and deep lakes is minimal. Water never compresses, even in the maximum ocean depths, to a degree of density that would prevent sinking objects from reaching the bottom.

As water freezes, expansion takes place, the final ice volume being at least 10% larger than the initial liquid mass. Fortunately because of the specific heat of water, the peculiarity of the solid state being lighter than the liquid state, and the reversal in density as the freezing temperature is reached (Fig.37), lakes, streams, and rivers freeze from the surface down. Only very small lakes and streams freeze completely solid during the winter months.

COLOR AND TRANSPARENCY

The color of lake water depends on depth, color of the surrounding area and sky, the scattered light rays coming from the water and in most cases, on absorption of the scattered light rays by dissolved or suspended materials. The most elaborate and accurate measurements of light penetration of lake water are now determined by a photocell. The old *Secchi disk* method uses a white disk 20 cm in diameter which is lowered into the lake until it disappears from view. The arithmetic mean of several attempts in slightly different locations, both of downward disappearance and upward reappearance, is the *Secchi disk transparency*. Even though "blue light" may penetrate to 1,200 ft. in the ocean (R. F. Dill, personal communication, 1967), tests by the Secchi disk show observations below 100 ft. are exceptional, even in the clearest waters, and in many turbid lakes a Secchi disk transparency of less than 1–3 ft. is common.

The color of lake water, due mainly to absorption and reflection of the sun's energy, may range from the "sky-blue water" of the northern lakes to the black of the Black Sea. Lake water is typically blue for pure, clear water, and various shades of blue-green to a definite green, then into the yellows and browns, the various colors produced by the innumerable contaminants (Table I). In general, black lake water results from a high organic content and blue lake water results from an absence of contaminating materials. The color of most lake water exists because of light scattering by the vibrant water molecules, the blue predominating because molecular scattering is greater for the shorter wave lengths. Water depth does not significantly influence

TABLE I

VARIATIONS IN WATER COLOR

(After SHAPIRO, 1956)

Color	Contaminants
Clear blue (pure water)	No contaminants of suspended materials; color due to molecular scattering
Greenish blue	
Bluish green	Suspension of blue–green algae, phytoplankton
Green	Colloidal $CaCO_3$ (hard water)
Yellowish green ⎱	⎰ Suspended sulfur
Greenish yellow ⎰	⎱ High plankton content excluding humic debris
Yellow	Diatoms
Yellow brown	Diatoms—fluorescent compounds, humic acids, carboxylic acids, organic matter
Brownish yellow	
Brown	
Gray	*Spirostomum*
Black	Organic debris, oxidation of ferrous iron, *Stentor*
Red to orange to purple	Suspended clays, ferrous hydroxide, *Oscillataria rubescens*, *Euglena sanquinea*, *Haematococcus pluviolis*, *Dunaliella salina*, *Bacterium halobium*, purple sulfur bacteria, zooplankton.

water color, within reason, in that water depth may increase ten-fold yet the visible light will remain concentrated around the 0.5μ wave length which is blue light (Fig.38). Water depth does decrease the transmittal of visible light, thus lending the dark or opaque color to the lake.

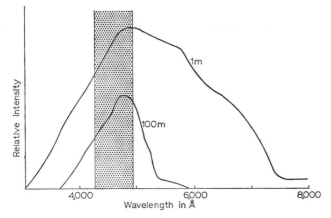

Fig.38. The relative intensity of light of different wave lengths (Å) at 1 and 100 m. The stippled area is blue light. (Modified after G. L. CLARKE, 1939. Copyright 1939 by the *Am. Assoc. Advan. Sci., Publ.*, 10.)

TEMPERATURE DISTRIBUTION

Temperature of the water in a lake basin is seldom constant, variations depending on depth, season, and geography, obvious exceptions being extremely
shallow playa-type lakes or lakes perpetually frozen. Lake water is heated by absorption of solar radiation, retaining the absorbed heat for unusually lengthy
periods of the high specific heat value (see p.39). Naturally the surface water heats
fastest until, in lakes of depth, the uppermost warm, moving (circulating) water has
a near-uniform temperature and is known as the *epilimnion* (BIRGE, 1910). Water
beneath the epilimnion, known as the *hypolimnion* (BIRGE, 1910), is cold and non-
circulating. The area where the temperature drops appreciably from the epilimnion
to the hypolimnion is the *thermocline* (BIRGE, 1897), the actual depth zone of maximum decrease in temperature termed the *metalimnion* (Fig.39).

Whether heated surface water mixes with colder water at depth depends on
the relative temperature difference at the thermocline. An average lake in the temperate latitudes experiences mixing or "turnover" in the early spring, mainly due to
strong winds. Sometime during the early spring the surface waters are at about the
same temperature as the deeper waters, thus mixing can take place. As the wind
blows surface water shoreward, currents deflect from the shore under the advancing
surface water and move along the lake bottom. However, as the season progresses
increased heating of the upper surface water decreases density (Fig.37) until, when
an appreciable temperature difference exists as during midsummer, the winds are
unable to mix the light warm waters with the underlying dense cold water.

A reverse situation then occurs as fall cooling takes place. The surface water

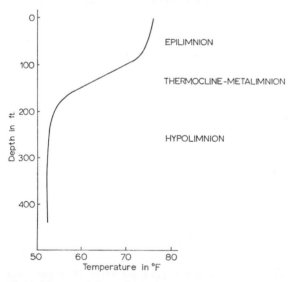

Fig.39. The actual thermal layering of Lake Meade, Arizona, September 29, 1948. (Modified after
HARBECK et al., 1958.)

slowly looses heat so that, in effect, the temperature and density differences on either side of the metalimnion become less. When the entire lake is at about the same temperature, and uniform density, wind-moved surface water once again starts forcing the metalimnion to greater depths, finally eliminating *thermal stratification* when the metalimnion reaches bottom. As surface cooling continues and temperatures fall below 4 °C, a fortunate inverse density difference exists (Fig.37) which allows the lake water to freeze from the surface downward instead of from the bottom up. If this inversion did not occur, the colder surface water would continually sink until freezing temperatures and, consequently, ice appeared over the lake bottom, the consequent increase in volume of the lake water as it froze forcing the overlying water out of the basin.

HUTCHINSON (1957) proposes the term *dimictic* for lakes which, due mainly to seasonal changes, circulate twice a year. Further refinement (HUTCHINSON, 1957) is given by the terminology *warm monomictic* and *cold monomictic*, or lakes that circulate during winter months at water temperatures over 4 °C (open lakes with associated ice) and lakes that circulate during summer months at water temperatures below 4 °C respectively. If a lake is perpetually covered by ice, as occurs in the polar regions, the term *amictic* is used. *Oligomictic* refers to lakes in the warm tropic areas where water temperature is consistantly high. A *polymictic* lake (HUTCHINSON and LÖFFLER, 1956) experiences circulation somewhat over 4 °C, a well-defined metalimnion failing to develop because of insignificant atmospheric temperature changes.

Many lakes exist which, usually because of shallow depth, fail to develop a metalimnion. HUTCHINSON (1957) considers a *first-class lake* those that are very deep and where temperature of the hypolimnion is near 4 °C, a *second-class* lake being shallower and allowing a decided seasonal variation in temperature of the hypolimnion (the minimum being about 4 °C), and a *third-class* lake as too shallow for development of a hypolimnion.

Water movements which persist after the dissipation of causative factors, such as strong winds or extraordinary barometric pressure changes, are known as *seiches* (sāsh). Most seiches are probably caused by friction of the wind, earthquakes, or barometric pressure changes but isolated examples of seiches caused by density slumps or an inrush of flood waters are known. Seiche records show maximum depths are usually in the range 20 to 40 cm with periods of 10–30 min. (HUTCHINSON, 1957), yet little is actually known of the effect of seiches on shape of lake basins. Because of small size, seiches are not expected to exert any great influence on lake basin orientation even though there is a damping effect as the water oscillations diminish by traveling back and forth across the basin; thus, seiches are presently of little interest to paleolimnologists principally because of this lack of knowledge.

Chapter 5

LACUSTRINE SEDIMENTS: CHEMICAL PRECIPITATES

The chemical composition of any lake water will ultimately depend on those elements and compounds in solution, in suspension, and those accumulating along the lake bottom, most of which come secondarily to the lakes by runoff. Other substances are produced by chemical reactions between the different elements and/or compounds as by vegetation growing in or around the lakes.

Water in closed lake basins is unlike the waters of other lakes in two respects: (*1*) it continually experiences a change in chemical composition because, (*2*) it continually increases its concentration of various salts, mainly due to a high evaporation rate. However, the increase in salts in a closed basin is not infinite. Certainly as water flows into the dry lake basin, perhaps with the first rains of late summer or early fall, it carries the salts from rock surrounding the lake basin and dissolves the surface salts of the playa, providing they have not been removed by deflation. Even so, this is the time when the waters of the closed basin are freshest. As precipitation declines, generally after the early spring rains, evaporation becomes greater than inflow which then starts the inevitable process of concentration of the salts in solution.

The salts concentrated in the waters of closed basins depend mainly on the rock type(s) of the surrounding basins and/or the chemical character of any influents, and to a minor degree on several inorganic ions in rain water (Fig.40–44). Generally, the salts deposited in closed lake basins are more or less the same as those in present ocean water, but there is a predominance of limestone ($CaCO_3$), dolomite $CaMg(CO_3)_2$,

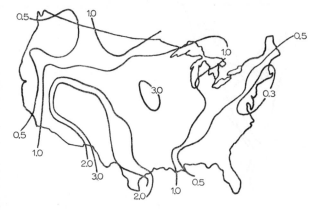

Fig.40. Average concentration of Ca^{2+} in mg/l in rain water during the period July, 1955–June, 1956. (Modified after JUNGE and WERBY, 1958.)

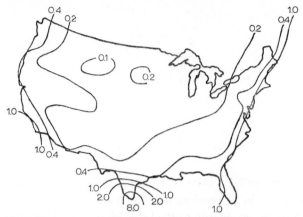

Fig.41. Average concentration Cl⁻ in mg/l in rain water during the period July, 1955–June, 1956. (Modified after JUNGE and WERBY, 1958.)

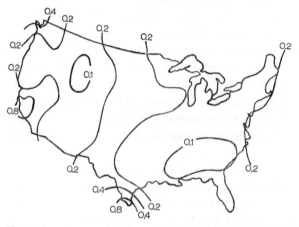

Fig.42. Average concentration of K⁺ in mg/l in rain water during the period July, 1955–June, 1956. (Modified after JUNGE and WERBY, 1958.)

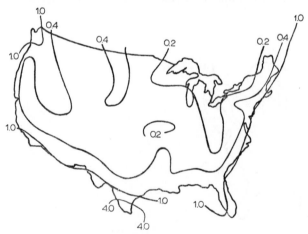

Fig.43. Average concentration of Na⁺ in mg/l in rain water during the period July, 1955–June, 1956 (Modified after JUNGE and WERBY, 1958.)

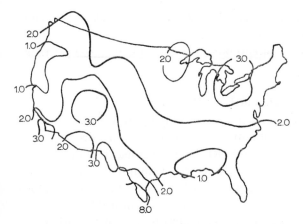

Fig.44. Average concentration of SO_4^{2-} in mg/l in rain water during the period July, 1955–June, 1956. (Modified after JUNGE and WERBY, 1958.)

and various sulphates. Extreme variance may often be produced by alternate deposition and resolution, desiccation of the playas, and chemistry of intermittent influents. The percent salinity between the Dead Sea (26%), Great Salt Lake (28%), the Red Sea (4%), and the world's oceans (3.5%), emphasizes the variance which actually occurs.

The normal chemical composition of average fresh river and average fresh lake waters as well as that of several well-known salt lakes is compared to that of sea water in Table II; the average composition of ocean salts is shown in Table III.

The products of chemical precipitation are controlled by several variables

TABLE II

PERCENTAGE COMPOSITION OF MAJOR IONS IN AVERAGE RIVER-LAKE COMPARED TO WATER IN SEVERAL WELL-KNOWN CLOSED BASINS AND AVERAGE SEA WATER

(After F. W. CLARKE, 1924; SVERDRUP et al., 1942; BRAITSCH, 1962)

Ions	River-lake	Great Salt Lake	Borax lake	Dead Sea	Owens Lake	Salton Sea	Sea water
CO_3^{2-}	33.40	0.09	22.47	trace	22.00	1.85	0.14
SO_4^{2-}	15.31	6.68	0.13	0.24	9.89	13.41	2.65
Cl^-	7.44	55.48	32.27	67.30	25.40	47.83	18.98
NO_3^-	1.15	—	—	—	—	—	—
Ca^{2+}	19.36	0.16	0.03	6.64	—	2.80	0.40
Mg^{2+}	4.87	2.76	0.35	15.92	—	1.81	1.27
Na^+	7.46	33.17	38.10	5.50	37.83	31.29	10.56
K^+	1.77	1.66	1.52	1.68	2.09	0.65	0.38
SiO	8.60	—	0.01	trace	0.20	0.26	—
$(Fe, Al)_2O_3$	0.64	—	0.01	—	—	0.02	—

including hydrogen-ion concentration (pH) and the oxidation–reduction potential (Eh). The concentration of hydrogen ions is naturally a measure of the acidity or alkalinity of water, the greater the concentration, the lower the pH. The pH ranges from a low of about 1 or 1.5 to a high of about 12 (most water in the range 6–9), but values below 4 seldom occur (HUTCHINSON, 1957). ATKINS (1930) listed the pH values of various environments as shown in Table IV.

Low pH values are produced by organic acids and H_2SO_4 while higher values are usually the result of carbonate saturation. Photosynthesis, by decreasing the CO_2 content of water, increases pH, thus extremely high values may result from active photosynthesis or presence of carbonates (usually magnesium and sodium) whose solubility exceeds that of $CaCO_3$. HUTCHINSON (1957) shows the molecular proportions of CO_2, HCO_3^-, and CO_3^{2-} at various pH values in a dilute solution at 15 °C. Since temperature is within reason, it is of interest to note that bicarbonate is important until the pH reaches about 9.0–9.5; however, most studies indicate that only the cations Mg^{2+}, Na^+, and K^+ are important when pH exceeds 9. Actually, presence of limestone in a lacustrine section indicates the past presence of a pH of at least 7.0 (KRUMBEIN and GARRELS, 1952). Six depositional environments are defined by CHILINGAR (1955) based on the pH: (1) strongly alkaline pH 9.0; (2) alkaline pH 8.0–9.0; (3) weakly alkaline pH 7.2–8.0; (4) neutral pH 6.6–7.2; (5) slightly acid pH 5.5–6.6; and (6) acid pH 2.1–5.5.

Study of present lakes shows vertical and horizontal changes in the pH and a relation between the type and concentration of lacustrine salts, thus it is reasonable to expect that ancient lakes might also have been so affected. However, the significance of such changes is probably not meaningfully reflected in the lacustrine section except by low pH values near vegetated shorelines allowing deposition of peat-type deposits or highly organic lacustrine muds.

The Eh refers to the oxidizing ability of the environment of deposition, measured in volts. A positive Eh is created by oxidation, a negative Eh is caused by reduction, the boundary between a reducing and oxidizing environment arbitrarily set at 0.20 V (RUTTNER, 1952). This is perhaps best explained by the oxidation of ferrous iron or the reduction of ferric iron, as in the equation ($Fe^{2+} \underset{\text{reduction}}{\overset{\text{oxidation}}{\rightleftarrows}} Fe^{3+}$ electrons). Because the Eh is closely tied to the temperature and pH (falling as temperature and pH increases), readings are always referred to pH 7. The particular ranges in Eh at which changes, either oxidation or reduction, take place in the chemical system common to lakes is found in Table V.

The literature is full of Eh–pH diagrams at set temperatures and pressures for practically all of the important carbonates, sulfides, oxides, and hydroxides. Rather than present these, when application to the quickly changing lacustrine environments is questionable, interested readers should refer to KRUMBEIN and GARRELS (1952), MARCHANDESE (1956), KRAUSKOPF (1957), GARRELS (1960), and GARRELS and CHRIST (1965).

TABLE III

AVERAGE COMPOSITION OF OCEAN SALTS

(After F. W. CLARKE, 1924)

Salt	%
NaCl	77.76
MgCl$_2$	10.88
MgSO$_4$	7.74
CaSO$_4$	3.60
K$_2$SO$_4$	2.46
CaCO$_3$	0.35
MgBr$_2$	0.22

TABLE IV

VARIOUS ENVIRONMENTS AND ASSOCIATED pH VALUES

(After ATKINS, 1930)

Environment	pH
Crater lake water with H$_2$SO$_4$	1.5
Peat and associated water	4.0–4.5
Rain water	5.9
Calcareous springs	6.0–6.6
Calcareous lake and river water	8.0–8.4
Calcareous-deficient lake/river water	6.5–7.0
Ponds with weeds	9.6
Surface of the sea	8.1–8.4
Alkali soil of Sudan	10.0

TABLE V

CONTROLLING REDOX-POTENTIAL RANGES OF CHEMICAL SYSTEMS COMMON TO LAKES

(After RUTTNER, 1962)

Systems	Range (V)
Fe^{2+}—Fe^{3+}	0.30—9.35
NO$_3$—NO$_2$	0.45—0.40
NO$_2$—NH$_3$	0.40—0.35
SO$_4$—S	0.10—0.06
Anaerobic bacteria present	0.4

Disregarding pH and Eh, temperature and solubility undoubtedly exercise predominant control over the sequence and products of chemical precipitates. Temperature is particularly important because precipitation of evaporites requires higher temperatures than normally evaporate pure water due to the reduction of vapor pressure caused by the brine. Because of this, deposition of chemical precipitates in a closed lake basin may then be expected to *somewhat* follow the order long ago stipulated by USIGLIO (1849) for average sea water. After some iron oxide, calcium and magnesium carbonates should be the first salts to precipitate, followed by gypsum ($CaSO_4 \cdot 2H_2O$). Excess Ca^{2+} and Na^+ present may then cause precipitation as pirssonite ($CaCO_3 \cdot Na_2CO_3 \cdot 2H_2O$) and gaylussite ($CaCO_3 \cdot Na_2CO_3 \cdot 5H_2O$), perhaps followed by trona ($Na_2CO_3 \cdot NaHCO_3 \cdot 2H_2O$). Halite preceeds the magnesium and sodium sulfates such as bloedite ($Na_2Mg(SO_4)_2 2H_2O$), mirabilite ($Na_2SO_4 \cdot 10H_2O$), and epsomite ($MgSO_4 \cdot 7H_2O$), followed by bischofite ($MgCl_2 \cdot 6H_2O$), sodium bromide (NaBr), and the last or soluble potassic (KCl) salts such as sylvite (KCl).

Certainly this orderly sequence never occurs in the oceans of the world and has only occurred in a very few of the ancient oceans, let alone in any closed lake basin. Experiments show that precipitation depends on such things as solubility of each salt in solution, concentration of each salt, and temperature, a simple KCl–NaCl solution well illustrating such changes. A KCl–NaCl solution will, on polythermal precipitation, show a gypsum/anhydrite boundary at 35 °C, but if the solution becomes enriched in Mg^{2+} the gypsum/anhydrite boundary is moved to about 45 °C (BORCHERT and MUIR, 1964).

Like ocean water most "salt lakes" are generally rich in Cl^-, Mg^{2+}, Na^+, K^+, and SO_4^{2-} ions which yield, in equilibrium in a saturated solution, only five solid phases (BRAITSCH, 1963). In present salt lakes the evaporite sequences tend to be

TABLE VI

THE COMMON LACUSTRINE EVAPORITE MINERALS AND THEIR TEMPERATURE STABILITY RANGES (IN THE QUINARY SYSTEM SATURATED WITH NaCl)

(Modified after BRAITSCH, 1963)

Mineral		Temperature	
		Lower	Upper
Anhydrite	$CaSO_4$	18	—
Bloedite	$Na_2Mg(SO_4)_2 \cdot 4H_2O$	4	59.5
Epsomite	$MgSO_4 \cdot 7H_2O$	< 0	28
Gypsum	$CaSO_4 \cdot 2H_2O$	< 0	18
Glauberite	$Na_2Ca(SO_4)_2$	10.5	> 100
Mirabilite	$Na_2SO_4 \cdot 10H_2O$	<0	26
Halite	NaCl	−2	⩾ 1,000
Thenardite	Na_2SO_4	13.5	> 100

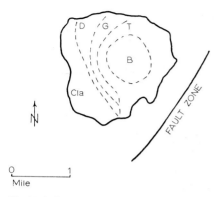

Fig.45. Saline mineral zoning at Deep Spring Lake, California. B = burkeite; T = thenardite; G = gaylussite; D = dolomite; Cla = calcite and/or aragonite. (Modified from B. F. JONES, 1965.)

TABLE VII

THE LACUSTRINE EVAPORITES

Mineral	Composition
Carbonates	
Limestone	$CaCO_3$
Aragonite	$CaCO_3$
Dolomite	$CaMG(CO_3)_2$
Natron*	$Na_2CO_3 \cdot 10H_2O$
Trona*	$Na_2CO_3 \cdot NaHCO_3 \cdot 2H_2O$
Sulfates	
Anhydrite	$CaSO_4$
Gypsum	$CaSO_4 \cdot 2H_2O$
Glauberite	$CaSO_4 \cdot Na_2SO_4$
Epsomite	$MgSO_4 \cdot 7H_2O$
Bloedite	$MgSO_4 \cdot Na_2SO_4 \cdot 4H_2O$
Thenardite	Na_2SO_4
Chlorides	
Halite	$NaCl$
Syvite*	KCl
Borates	
Borax*	$Na_2B_4O_7 \cdot 1OH_2O$
Searlesite*	$Na_2O \cdot B_2O_3 \cdot 4SiO_2 \cdot 2H_2O$
Colemanite*	$Ca_2B_6O_{11} \cdot 5H_2O$
Nitrates	
Soda niter*	$NaNO_3$
Niter*	KNO_3

* Most uncommon lacustrine evaporites.

metastable, yet in fossil strata the evaporites contain only the stable phases (BRAITSCH, 1963), therefore, depositional temperature is probably in most cases masked by the temperature of evaporite diagenesis. Table VI, listing the common lacustrine evaporite minerals with their temperature stability ranges in the quinary system when saturated with NaCl, is then given only to present some idea of the temperature limits for the various minerals under the prescribed conditions.

An excellent discussion of stable evaporite phases, and of the transition temperatures from one phase to another is too advanced for this preliminary work; however, those wishing to pursue the subject further are advised to examine BRAITSCH (1962).

All closed lakes with evaporating saline waters must, at some time, sequentially deposit their salts, but generally no investigator is present to observe the depositional sequence or the salts become redissolved and mixed due to local runoff before their presence is either realized or studied. B. F. JONES (1965) investigated salt zoning at Death Valley and Deep Spring Lake, California, Fig.45, showing the zoning of salts over the playa of Deep Spring Lake. Fig.46, an aerial photograph of the great Lake Eyre basin, South Australia, illustrates a monomineralic zoning process, but in this case the salt is mainly halite.

Fig.46. A 120-sq. mile salt water remnant in Belt Bay, Lake Eyre, South Australia. Notice the concentric rings of salt (mainly halite) deposited as the playa waters evaporate. (Photo by courtesy of C. Warren Bonython.)

Closed lakes are generally not saturated with salts other than calcium carbonate and gypsum, although because of a rapid decrease in solubility, the magnesium sulfate mirabilite is generally precipitated in closed lake basins of Canada and the western United States during the winter months. Because the solubility of halite does not appreciably increase as does the solubility of mirabilite, a reversal in the depositional order may occur if temperatures are particularly high in the day time and low at night. Such is the case in many of the pluvial basins of the southern High Plains, Texas, where long prismatic crystals or mirabilite line the shores during the cool early morning hours only to quickly disappear as the rising sun warms the water.

The presence of evaporites in an ancient lake basin, sometimes with the exception of the carbonates, indicates that the basin was closed; the longer the period of time the basin was closed, the thicker the evaporites providing inflow was supplying the necessary materials. Of course, if quantity of dissolved solids was rather low only thin evaporitic sections would have resulted. Thus, there is actually a close, but intangible, relation between amount of dissolved solids brought to a basin, size of the basin, and time presented by the lacustrine section. However, extreme caution must be exercised when attempting to correlate thickness of lacustrine sediments or amount of dissolved solids to time or rate of deposition and consequently age of the basin, for the larger basins do not necessarily contain the thickest lacustrine sections. A good case in point is Lake Eyre, South Australia, its 3,700 sq. mile playa containing salines with a maximum thickness of only about 15 ft. (JOHNS and LUDBROOK, 1962).

Evaporites are easily divided into five important groups: (*1*) carbonates, (*2*) sulfates, (*3*) chlorides, (*4*) borates, and (*5*) nitrates. Each group necessarily consists of many different minerals, however, the number of *common* lacustrine evaporites is generally less than the number of marine evaporites, but the variability of unusual lacustrine accumulations such as at Searles Lake, California, puts the marine evaporitic sequences to shame. The lacustrine evaporites to be discussed are listed in Table VII, those marked by an asterisk being the most uncommon.

CALCIUM CARBONATE

Deposition of lacustrine calcium carbonate can be in the form of *calcite* or *aragonite*. Of the two, only calcite is stable at usual atmospheric pressure and temperatures (JAMIESON, 1953; MacDONALD, 1956; DEER et al., 1962).

The deposition of lacustrine calcite or aragonite depends on saturation of the lake water with calcium (Ca^{2+}) and bicarbonate (HCO_3^-) ions, but whether aragonite (inorganic) is deposited instead of calcite (or vice versa) depends, if analogous to calcite–aragonite relations in the ocean, on supersaturation of the lake water (CLOUD, 1962a). ZELLER and WRAY (1956) find aragonite forming rather than calcite when rapid precipitation or high pH and salinity occurs, thus lacustrine aragonite laminae may indicate fresh water flooding of a saline lake. Several workers suggest the presence of Sr^{2+} in the water controls mineralogy, but CLOUD (1962a,b) finds aragonite precipitating when the water reaches super-saturation of the aragonite whose solubility under normal conditions exceeds that of calcite. For a still unknown reason, calcite *does not* precipitate once its saturation is exceeded when aragonite is present, a situation perhaps analagous to the refusal of dolomite to precipitate once super-saturation is reached in the presence of calcite. Supposedly the warm temperature of evaporation and high gypsum content of many closed lake basins favor deposition of aragonite, the calcium carbonate, and calcium sulfates[1], Sr^{2+} and Mg^{2+} ions transforming the aragonite to calcite (PALACHE et al., 1951; HUTCHINSON, 1957). Alteration of aragonite proceeds rapidly under humid conditions or high temperatures (GRAF and LAMAR, 1959), thus it should be unusual to find aragonite in ancient lake basins. The occurrence of aragonite then in the Great Salt Lake and Searles Lake basins, *thinolite* in the Lahontan basin, and calcite and dolomite in the pluvial basins of West Texas may have a significant environmental connotation[2] or may simply have resulted from the complexities attendant to carbonate deposition.

The solubility of the resulting calcium carbonate, which forms as shown by this equation is still imperfectly known:

$$Ca^{2+} + 2HCO_3^- \rightleftharpoons CaCO_3 + CO_2 + H_2O$$

even for sea water (CLOUD, 1962a,b; PYTOKOWICY, 1964; GARRELS and CHRIST, 1965) and thus only inferred for saline lakes. As in the oceans, solubility depends on temperature, pressure, and salinity, but in saline lakes variable salinities due to different salts often exist in water that may be supersaturated with other minerals, like dolomite. Therefore, although the kinetics are much different between ocean and closed lake water precipitation of carbonates, enough similarities exist to warrant comparison.

The sea water alkalinity exerts the principal influence on solubility of calcium carbonate, followed by temperature and pressure (DEGENS, 1965). Certainly anything tending to lower CO_2 content or increase pH contributes to precipitation of the carbonate, although most of the variables controlling precipitation of calcite by super-saturation of sea water fail to occur because of the interference of Mg^{2+} ions, precipitation depending mainly on biologic activity. However, when fresh water is supersaturated with calcium carbonate, precipitation apparently occurs in response to an increase in pH, a decrease in solubility of $CaCO_3$, a decrease in the solubility of CO_2, or a decrease in pressure produced perhaps by lake "turnover." Certainly in fresh water much carbonate precipitation occurs due to photosynthesis.

Precipitation by photosynthesis results from a sequence of events normal to many lakes. Carbon dioxide is brought to the lake by sheetwash and tributaries, both of which usually contain calcium in the (unstable) bicarbonate form. Thus, in many lakes bicarbonate (HCO_3^-) is the predominant anion and Ca^{2+} the predominant

---

[1] DEGENS (1965) finds calcium sulfate increases the stability of aragonite.
[2] Calcite indicative of deposition in colder water than aragonite.

cation, perhaps with some associated Mg^{2+}. Aquatic vegetation utilizes the CO_2 and the HCO_3^- which raises the pH. This causes precipitation of the $CaCO_3$ once pH exceeds a value of about 9, as shown by the equation:

$$Ca^{2+} + 2HCO_3^- \rightarrow CaCO_3 + CO_2 + H_2O$$

because of the disassociation of the HCO_3^- ion. The $CaCO_3$ is deposited and the CO_2 assimilated by local plants. The complete chemical details of photosynthesis are not known, but the equation explains the basic principles whereby carbohydrates:

$$6H_2O + CO_2 = C_6H_{12}O_6 + O_2$$

and oxygen are produced by utilization of the CO_2 content of the water by the plants.

Of course the reduction of the CO_2 causes precipitation of calcium carbonates. The algae, particularly *Charae* and *Cladophora*, account for most extensive lacustrine tufa deposits; however, other species are present. For instance, the limestone reefs in the Green River Formation were formed by *Cylorellopsis coloniate* REIS (BRADLEY, 1928). Algae most commonly associated with lacustrine carbonates are the blue-green Cyanophyceae, *Dichothrix calcarea*, *Fusciculata cleocapsa*, *Gongrosira*, *Lyngoya nana*, *Lyngbya martensiana calcaria*, *Phormidium*, *Revularia*, *Hematites*, *Schiyothrix fasciculata*, *Thoypothrix* (WEST, 1927; FRITSCH, 1959). Some precipitation of $CaCO_3$ by phytoplankton such as diatoms[1] and Coccolithophoridae occurs in many lakes but deposition of carbonate by photosynthesis or by algae is probably more widespread. The tufa deposits of Soap Lake, Washington, Mono Lake, California, Lake Lahontan, Nevada, Searles Lake, California, and of the Salton Sea are all considered of algal origin (RUSSELL, 1893; J. C. JONES, 1914, 1925; DUNN, 1953; SCHOLL, 1960).

Many aquatic flowering plants show, by encrustations of calcium carbonate on their leaves and stems, that they also influence the carbonate cycle, some producing as much as 2% of their weight in $CaCO_3$ each day. Certain plants, such as *Potamogeton*

TABLE VIII

CHEMICAL REACTIONS ALLOWING PRECIPITATION OF $CaCO_3$ BY BACTERIA, AS SUGGESTED BY VARIOUS EARLY INVESTIGATORS

(After CLOUD, 1962a)

Reference	Reaction
MURRAY and IRVINE, 1889	$(NH_4)_2CO_3 + CaSO_4 \rightarrow CaCO_3 + (NH_4)_2SO_4$
KELLERMAN and SMITH, 1914	$Ca(HCO_3)_2 + 2 NH_4OH \rightarrow CaCO_3 + 2H_2O + (NH_4)_2CO_3$
BERKELEY, 1919	$Ca(COOCH_3)_2 + 4O_2 \rightarrow CaCO_3 + 3CO_2 + 3H_2O$

[1] Diatoms (class Bacillariales), small siliceous algae, are often found in lacustrine strata of either fresh or saline origin, their presence generally a good indication of cool water.

Fig.47. A thin, indurated lentil of ripple-marked lacustrine limestone, Lynn County, Texas. The limestone is underlaid by Pearlette-like volcanic ash (pick head). Uncorrected radiocarbon dates on the limestone range from 34,400 to > 37,000 years B.P. (Photo by the author.)

Fig.48. Algal pinnacles at Searles Lake, California, formed by precipitation of carbonate by algae around submarine springs of pluvial Lake Searles. (Photo by D. W. Scholl.)

and *Elodea*, are constantly covered by a carbonate crust, while others, such as *Aratophyllum* and *Potamogeton*, have only slight encrustations of carbonate deposited within the plant tissues.

Many investigators believe $CaCO_3$ deposition in sea water can be caused by bacteria (ZoBELL, 1964), but CLOUD (1962a,b) considers bacteria as agents which mainly influence the CO_2 and calcium equilibria. Table VIII summarizes the chemical reactions considered essential to bacterial precipitation of $CaCO_3$.

Lacustrine limestone generally occurs in three main varieties: (*1*) as thin, widespread lentils or laminae (Fig.47), (*2*) as massive local wedges (Fig.48), and (*3*) as tufa (Fig.49). The thin laminae and massive wedges usually occur along and near-shore in larger lakes because of more rapid increases in temperature and/or pH and photosynthetic activity. The laminae, especially when alternating with zones of lacustrine clay containing other evaporites (Fig.50), are diagnostic of chemical stratification of the ancient lake. This was caused by accumulation of a layer of fresh bicarbonate-rich (storm?) water over a lower layer of dense, saline lake water, mixing having caused precipitation of the carbonate. This situation is ideally illustrated by the Searles Lake, California (SMITH, 1966) or Rita Blanca, Texas (ANDERSON and KIRKLAND, 1966) occurrences. The limestone masses (Fig.50) are formed by the contact of calcium-rich fresh water with saline lake water, thus usually mark ancient lake influents or areas where considerable surface drainage (sheetwash) has entered the lake. Lacustrine tufa, which was classified by RUSSELL (1887) and SCHOLL (1960), depends primarily on spring activity, thus geographic location in the lake basin depends on the local water table, impermeable strata, and faults and joints.

Fig.49. Local massive wedges of lacustrine limestone are generally due either to a delta-type deposit or spring activity. This boulder from an abandoned shoreline of pluvial Lake Palomas, Chihuahua, Mexico, is typical of spring-deposited tufa. (Photo by the author.)

Fig.50. Late Wisconsin laminated marl from the west side of Searles Valley, California, white laminae consisting mostly of aragonite, intervening layers of calcite, aragonite, dolomite, clastics, and organic material. Pairs of light and dark layers may represent annual cycles. (Photo by U.S. Geological Survey, by courtesy of G. I. Smith.)

In many areas where there has been intermittent lacustrine and aeolian deposition thin lentils of generally calcium carbonate frequently occur in the aeolian sands or loess immediately over the lacustrine sections. Examination will usually show such units to be caliche zones and not lacustrine carbonates.

Caliche forms in single or multiple layers in aggrading pedocal soils on the downwind side of regional desert areas due to calcification of carbonate-rich loess (REEVES, 1967). Formation of caliche requires a climate where evaporation greatly exceeds precipitation, thus caliche is commonly found around paleolake basins, lacustrine sections themselves often showing a caliche profile at surface. Care must be exercised not to confuse caliche with lacustrine carbonates nor to let calichification of a normal lacustrine section camouflage its true origin.

DOLOMITE

Dolomite differs from limestone only in that every other Ca^{2+} ion is replaced by a Mg^{2+} ion parallel to the C axis of the hexagonal cell, but in the direction perpendicular to the C axis we see layers of Ca^{2+} alternating with layers of Mg^{2+} ions.

Several investigations (FAIRBRIDGE, 1957; CLOUD, 1962a,b; INGERSON, 1962) have attempted to resolve the presence of vast quantities of ancient dolomite with the general absence of Recent marine dolomites, but the depositional environment for dolomite precipitation is still imperfectly known. Like calcium bicarbonate, magnesium usually occurs in lake water as a bicarbonate; however, a great difference in solubility exists between $MgCO_3$ and $CaCO_3$, the $CaCO_3$ being the least soluble of the two.

Dolomite is known to be stable at surface pressures and temperatures (ZEN, 1960), but attempts to precipitate dolomite in the laboratory under simulated marine, lacustrine, and/or lagoonal environments have consistently failed. It is interesting to note that several investigators (KAZAKOV et al., 1957; DUNBAR and RODGERS, 1957; CHILINGAR, 1956) have produced dolomite by greatly increasing the CO_2 partial pressure. Although the amount of atmospheric CO_2 may have been much greater during the early Paleozoic, partial pressure was probably never high enough for natural precipitation of dolomite (UREY, 1956).

Chemical reactions occur only in the direction of the negative free energy, thus

Fig.51. Close-up of the wall of a pit dug in the presently forming primary soft sediment dolomite Mound playa, Lynn and Terry Counties, Texas. Notice the pods and stringers of dolomite which, as they grow, cause displacement of the overlying 6 inches of playa sand. (Photo by T. R. Bates.)

the reactions between magnesium and calcium carbonates, when considered thermodynamically, lend clarity to the occurrence of dolomite. In very alkaline lake waters magnesium carbonate ($MgCO_3$) and calcium carbonate ($CaCO_3$) should form dolomite ($CaMg(CO_3)_2$). If the magnesium carbonate is in the form of nesquehonite ($MgCO_3 \cdot 3H_2O$), which KAZAKOV et al. (1957) consider stable at normal temperature, dolomite should also be produced with excess water. If the calcium carbonate is in the form of aragonite ($CaCO_3$), conversion takes place more readily because the instability of aragonite (CLOUD, 1962a,b).

No Recent dolomites, either lacustrine or marine, were known until STRAKHOV's (1953) report on Lake Balkhash. Recent and Quaternary authigenic dolomites are now known to be forming or have recently formed in the Coorong of South Australia (ALDERMAN and SKINNER, 1957; SKINNER, 1963) in Deep Spring Lake, California (PETERSON et al., 1963) on the west coast of the Persian Gulf (WELLS, 1962; CURTIS et al., 1963), on Sugarloaf Key, South Florida (SHINN, 1964), on Bonaire Island, Netherlands Antilles (DEFFEYES et al., 1964), in Great Salt Lake (BISSELL and CHILINGAR, 1962; GRAF et al., 1961), in Salt Flat Graben, Texas (FRIEDMAN, 1966) and in pluvial lake basins (Fig.51) of West Texas (REEVES and PARRY, 1965; PARRY and REEVES, 1966). All such Recent dolomites originated in hypersaline environments and all, other than those of the West Texas area, are unique in that they are poorly ordered (protodolomite). Older lacustrine dolomites also occur in the West Texas pluvial lake basins, in Lake Eyre, South Australia, and undoubtedly in many other paleolake basins in other parts of the world, but little is yet known of their mineralogy or chronology.

Fig.52. Typical thin indurated lacustrine carbonate (dolomite) on the south side of the island, Rich Lake, Terry County, Texas. Formed by desiccation of Rich Lake during the Vigo Park interval of mid-Tahoka time. Radiocarbon dates on this unit range from 17,400 to 18,000 years B.P. (Photo by the author.)

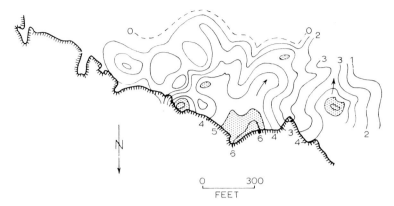

Fig.53. Isopachous map (as of June 1, 1967) of a pre-Tahoka dolomite wedge, north side, Mound playa, Mound Lake, Texas. The full extent of the dolomite on the east, west, and south is not as yet known. Thickest areas (stippled) are associated with present or ancient springs. Arrows show direction of present spring flow.

Protodolomite, with its weak or absent ordering X-ray diffraction peaks, excess of Ca^{2+} ions, and diffuse X-ray diffractions from planes perpendicular to the C axis (GRAF and GOLDSMITH, 1956), apparently forms before well-ordered stoichiometric dolomite, but whether protodolomite is always primary or secondary has not yet been resolved. PETERSON et al., (1963) consider calcite and aragonite in Deep

Fig.54. Local intermittent flooding of the north edge of Mound playa, Lynn and Terry Counties, Texas, by carbonate-rich spring water. A wedge of dolomite (outlined by the dashed line) underlies this area, most recent dolomite formation taking place directly below presently flooded areas. (Photo by the author.)

Spring Lake, California, are dissolved and reprecipitated by the magnesium-rich lake waters as primary dolomite. DEFFEYES et al., (1964) think the Recent dolomite on Bonaire Island results from a high magnesium/calcium ratio hypersaline brine, and BERNER (1965) finds dolomite beneath Pacific Ocean atolls the result of reflux of hypersaline brine. In general, oxygen and carbon isotope studies on coexisting calcites and dolomites from Recent (DEGENS and EPSTEIN, 1964) and Paleozoic dolomites (WEBER, 1964) indicate that dolomites are formed by metasomatic replacement of calcite and/or aragonite.

Unlike previous lacustrine carbonates, those from pluvial lake basins in West Texas are more or less well-ordered, the carbonate always being dolomite unless associated with volcanic ash falls (REEVES and PARRY, 1965). Soft sediment dolomite is presently forming in many of the West Texas pluvial lake basins due to runoff from intermittent influents, springs, and bordering sand dunes, although thin dolomite lentils have also formed during past periods of lake desiccation (Fig.52). The soft sediment, pre-Tahoka dolomite wedge, with a Recent-aged surface, Lake Mound, Texas, is probably the largest and best example of such "chemical deltas" (Fig.53);

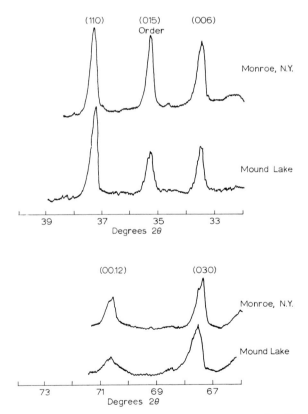

Fig.55. X-ray diffraction of the Mound Lake, Texas, soft sediment dolomite compared to the Monroe, New York, dolomite. The upper diagrams illustrate the weak ordering peaks, the lower diagrams show the diffuse nature of the (00.12) axis with nickel filtered copper radiation.

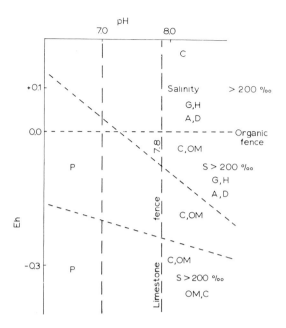

Fig.56. The carbonate environment and principal sedimentary materials related to select Eh and pH values. *C* = calcite; *G* = gypsum; *A* = anhydrite; *H* = halite; *D* = dolomite; *OM* = organic matter; *P* = peat; *S* = salinity. (Modified after KRUMBEIN and GARRELS, 1952.)

surface precipitation is due to the flooding of the playa by carbonate-rich spring water (Fig.54). The spring water seeps into the permeable surface sands of the playa, concomitant evaporation and contact with playa brines causing precipitation of dolomite, first as isolated stringers and pods which cause deformation of overlying lacustrine sediments (Fig.51). Although ordering X-ray diffractions are weak and diffractions from planes perpendicular to the *C* axis are diffuse (Fig.55), there is no excess of Ca^{2+} ions. The Mound Lake dolomite, considered purely on the basis of chemistry, is therefore the first true primary stoichiometric lacustrine dolomite. This contention is supported by isotopic studies and uniform grain size, absence of porosity, fauna, textures, fine laminations, and pure white color, all characteristics of primary "dolostones" (WEBER, 1964).

For lacustrine carbonates we find that the calcium and carbonate ions are little effected by the Eh but greatly controlled by the pH. The vigorous disassociation of carbonates with even gentle acids precludes their deposition in environments of pH less than 7.0, and some investigations (KRUMBEIN and GARRELS, 1952) suggest a pH of at least 7.0. Fig. 56, modified from KRUMBEIN and GARRELS (1952), shows the carbonate environment based on pH–Eh associations, the upper right hand field corresponding to normal marine conditions. If closed lake deposition operates with waters chemically similar to the sea, most lacustrine carbonates then must represent environments of pH < 7.8 and Eh no less than about −0.1. Whether the carbonate is limestone or dolomite depends on availability of Mg^{2+} ions.

Lacustrine dolomite also forms as thin, near-shore lentils during lake desiccation (Fig.52). The formation of dolomite in this manner provides not only a valuable environmental clue but a significant stratigraphic horizon which generally can be easily correlated from basin to basin on a regional scale.

GYPSUM

Evaporation of normal sea water first yields calcium carbonate followed by calcium sulfate ($CaSO_4 \cdot 2H_2O$), but in many saline lakes calcium sulfate may be the first salt to appear. Certainly, in saline lakes as well as in the ocean, calcium sulfate will precipitate at normal pressures and temperatures before other sulfate salts, for solubility decreases greatly for anhydrite ($CaSO_4$) with increasing temperature, the anhydrite precipitating at temperatures over about 42 °C providing an absence of other electrolytes. POSNYAK (1940), D'ANS et al., (1955), and BRAITSCH (1962), as well as others, show anhydrites may precipitate at temperatures as low as 7 °C in the presence of foreign electrolytes; however, absence of surface anhydrite deposits, whether marine or lacustrine, indicates that such precipitation is impossible. Many present lake waters, as found in Switzerland, West Texas, eastern New Mexico and New York, are rich in gypsum, but it is in the ancient lake basins of the world that the vast lacustrine gypsum deposits occur. Lake Eyre, Australia, is estimated to contain at least 4,000 million tons (BONYTHON, 1956; TERMIER and TERMIER, 1963) and beds of gypsum up to 150 feet thick are known in the Ued Rir (GRABAU, 1924). Surface occurrences of selenite crystals, and large gypsum dunes, also exist in the Sahara, Africa, throughout much of Australia, in northern Chihuahua, Mexico, and throughout West Texas and the southwestern deserts of the United States, but the subsurface extent of the gypsum, for the most part, is unknown. Extensive gypsum deposits, and particularly those mined for use in the building trades, were produced by the evaporation of enclosed seas: such gypsum is generally of the rock, gypsite, or satin spar type. Gypsum of lacustrine origin, for some unknown reason, is characteristically of the selenite type (Fig.57).

The size of lacustrine gypsum crystals, like the size of most chemically precipitated crystals, ranges considerably. Many variables, such as water chemistry, temperature, and kinetic factors, control the size of chemically precipitated crystals. In general we can suspect that precipitation from supersaturated solutions will form a multiplicity of small crystals (BUCKLEY, 1951; LA MER, 1952; MILLIN, 1961), such a condition generally occurring during rapid evaporation of a lake. Likewise, very slow evaporation or biologic activity may cause a slower crystallization rate allowing growth of larger crystals (Fig.58), the position of the crystal being a good clue as to its origin. Irregularly large crystals transverse to the bedding are best considered the result of biologic precipitation of sulfates. Certainly the different minerals are differently affected by the various variables to a degree that prevents development of

Fig.57. Large wedges of selenite gypsum oriented more or less perpendicular to bedding of lacustrine clay, Lynn County, Texas. Origin due to biologic activity, growth of crystals taking place in desiccation cracks. (Photo by the author.)

generalized "rules of crystallization." For instance, some minerals simply tend to crystallize in smaller sizes than others.

All lake waters contain the sulfate radical (SO_4^{2-}) because of its presence in rain (Fig.44), but supersaturation of lake water by sulfate must arise from other contributory reasons. For instance, deposition of several tens or hundreds of feet of gypsum in a lake would suggest weathering of marine salts, recharge of the lake by salt-saturated subterranean waters, salt-saturated influents, wind-transported salts, or perhaps that the lake basin was once connected to an ancient sea.

Whether gypsum will be deposited in a lake depends on the concentration of sulfate, the concentration of calcium, and somewhat on the presence of hydrogen sulfide (H_2S). Certainly if the concentration of sulfate is below saturation, gypsum ($CaSO_4 \cdot 2H_2O$) could not precipitate, and if all available calcium were tied up in the deposition of the earlier carbonates, none would be available to unite with the

Fig.58. Large gypsum intergrowths of probable biologic origin in playa sand sediments of pluvial Lake Palomas, Salinas, Chihuahua, Mexico. Thickness of gypsum bed unknown. (Photo by the author.)

sulfate. Fortunately enough calcium is commonly present in most saline lakes to insure the precipitation of gypsum providing the lake can reach the saturation of gypsum. Because gypsum is the least soluble of the sulfates under ordinary conditions, precipitation usually occurs immediately without any chemical intricacies.

If lake basin sediments contain appreciable quantities of fragmental or sedimentary pyrite oxidation may provide sulfate per the following equations:

$$4FeS_2 + 15O_2 + 2H_2O \rightarrow 2Fe_2(SO_4)_3 + 2H_2SO_4$$

$$2FeS_2 + 7O_2 + 2H_2O \rightarrow 2FeSO_4 + 2H_2SO_4$$

Because most saline lakes contain appreciable quantities of carbonate the sulfuric acid produced will generally react with the carbonate to form gypsum in the following manner:

$$H_2SO_4 + CaCO_3 + 2H_2O \rightarrow CaSO_4 \cdot 2H_2O + H_2CO_3$$

The production of hydrogen sulfide (H_2S) generally occurs due to decomposition (reduction) of vegetative matter by bacteria (usually a species of genus *Desulfovibrio*)[1]

---

[1] A new classification for sulfate-reducing bacteria has been proposed: see CAMPBELL and POSTGATE (1965) and POSTGATE and CAMPBELL (1966).

in the lake sediments or on the lake bottom. If the lake is shallow, H_2S formed by reduction on the bottom will go into solution and oxidize, due probably to the genus *Thiobacillus*, and sulfide in the muds will bleed to the water as sulfate. Hydrogen sulfide formed in lake sediments or in deep lakes will accumulate, oxidation to sulfate finally occurring at a much later date. In many saline lakes fermentation of organic debris under anaerobic conditions produces hydrogen which, with the available sulfate, causes formation of H_2S in bottom muds as the equation:

$$5H_2 + SO_4 \rightarrow H_2S \downarrow + 4H_2O$$

Pure sulfur, though generally in minor amounts, often occurs in the muds of anaerobic lakes, precipitation due to oxidation of FeS or H_2S as:

$$3H_2S + 2Fe^{3+} \rightarrow 6H^+ + 2FeS + S \downarrow$$

FeS precipitates when iron, either ferrous of ferric, is present although when the iron is present additional free sulfur is precipitated. Free sulfur may also form in anaerobic lake clays by microbiological and chemical changes of gypsum crystals. BAAS-BECKING and KAPLAN (1956) show the formation of the Lake Eyre sulfur nodules discovered by Bonython (BONYTHON and KING, 1956) resulting from the reaction:

$$CaSO_4 \cdot 2H_2O + 8H + CO_2 + Fe(OH)_2 \rightarrow FeS + CaCO_3 + 7H_2O$$

due to halophilic sulfate reducing bacteria. The FeS then oxidizes as:

$$4FeS + 3O_2 \rightarrow 2Fe_2O_3 + 4S \downarrow$$

Bacteria which oxidize sulfur compounds belong to the Beggiatoaceae, Nitrobacteriaceae, and Pseudomonadaceae families. The important genus is *Thiobacillus* (family Nitrobacteriaceae), species *denitrificans, novellus, coproliticus, thioparus,* and *thiooxidans*. Although evidence is still somewhat questionable it appears that formation of sulfur may take place because of oxidation of thiosulfate as shown by STARKEY's (1935) equation, or by the oxidation of FeS as shown above:

$$5Na_2S_2O_3 + H_2O + 4O_2 \rightarrow 5Na_2SO_4 + H_2SO_4 + 4S$$

HALITE

Deposits of halite (NaCl), often thousands of feet thick, have resulted from desiccation of enclosed seas, but halite deposits from saline lakes though common, are seldom over a few tens of feet thick at most. Certain ancient lake basins contain

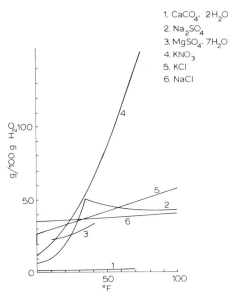

Fig.59. Solubility curves in water for several of the common and a few of the rarer lacustrine salts. (Modified after BRISCOE, 1951.)

extensive halite deposits, for instance 500 million tons alone in the surface crust of Lake Eyre, Australia (BONYTHON and MASON, 1953), about $12 \cdot 10^{10}$ tons in the Dead Sea (ARMSTRONG and MIALL, 1946), and about 6 billion tons of principally NaCl in the Bonneville Basin (EARDLEY et al., 1957). Rather pure deposits of halite occur in the Great Salt Plain of Lop, Eastern Turkestan, and in many salines of the Sahara, Central Africa, and throughout the Kalahari (PASSARGE, 1904). Particularly pure halite is deposited in many of the salt lakes of Astrakhan District, Russia. Many ancient lake basins, at least in the western United States, exhibit a decided absence of halite, probably because of the great difference between the solubility of gypsum and halite. In pure water at about 10 °C, the solubility of gypsum is only 1.90 g/kg compared to a solubility of 35.8 g/kg for halite (Fig.59). A secondary reason is probably the low concentration of the Cl⁻ ion in the average lake and the low Ca^{2+} ion concentration remaining in lake brines after precipitation of the carbonates and sulfates. A similar absence of halite generally occurs in the pluvial lake basins of West Texas, the only ones known to contain considerable halite being basins near Loving, New Mexico and Brownfield, Texas, which accumulate waste dumped by nearby potash and sodium sulfate plants.

Many lakes, like Owens and Mono Lakes, California, Lake Goodenough, Saskatchewan, Canada, and other soda or sodium sulfate lakes throughout the world, contain subterranean brines that frequently have a greater per cent halite than any other salt. Searles Lake, California, which contains about 3 billion tons of salts, has brines containing about 16% NaCl, and brines from pluvial lake basins on the southern High Plains of West Texas average about 6–14% NaCl. NaCl content in the sodium sulfate brines of North Dakota average about 4%.

Halite normally precipitates in regular cubes; however, impurities, which cause changes in the surface tension and pH of the precipitating fluid (VAN HOOK, 1961) or extreme supersaturation, will cause precipitation of octahedral halite faces.

SODIUM AND MAGNESIUM CARBONATE AND SULFATE SALTS

Bitter lakes contain considerable quantities of sodium sulfate and *alkali lakes* contain predominantly sodium carbonate, but distinction between the two is often difficult because of the general occurrence of significant quantities of SO_4^{2-}, CO_3^{2-}, Na^+, Cl^-, Mg^{2+}, and K^+. Such a complex mixture then allows, dependant on climatic environment, precipitation of many different salts.

Lakes and/or lake basins rich in sodium sulfate are common to all arid regions of the world and, in the United States, are found mainly in California, Oregon, New Mexico, Wyoming, Utah, and Texas, but also exist in great numbers in Canada and Mexico (Fig.60). Soda and Searles Lakes, California, examples from a hot, arid area, contain as much as 88% anhydrous sulfate (BATEMAN, 1956; EUGSTER and SMITH, 1965), Soda Lake alone containing nearly a million tons (BORCHERT and MUIR, 1964).

In cold arid regions, such as Wyoming and North Dakota, sodium sulfate deposits are usually in the form of Glauber's salt (mirabilite—$Na_2SO_4 \cdot 10H_2O$), since solubility of mirabilite decreases tremendously between 33° and −5 °C, but when exposed in a dry basin the sodium sulfate will lose its water, going to anhydrous thenardite (Na_2SO_4). Great Salt Lake, Utah, is underlaid by a 32-ft. layer of mirabilite which extends some 9½ miles (EARDLEY, 1962), mirabilite even piling up alongshore during the cold winter months (Fig.61). Fig.59 shows sodium sulfate is more soluble than halite in water above 32 °C, thus if deposition occurs in warm arid areas sodium sulfate (thenardite) would probably follow deposition of salt (NaCl). However, below 32 °C sodium sulfate is *not* as soluble as halite, thus at low temperatures precipitation of mirabilite preceeds that of halite. This is more or less why Searles Lake, California, contains thenardite and the lakes of Saskatchewan, Canada, and North Dakota, contain mirabilite.

Whether magnesium sulfate (epsomite $MgSO_4 \cdot 7H_2O$) precipitates depends mainly on the presence of excess Mg^{2+} after precipitation of the carbonates. In average river water the cations are usually in the proportion where Ca^{2+} exceeds Mg^{2+} (which may or may not exceed Na^+), which exceeds K^+, but saline lake waters may be quite different, depending on previously precipitated salts, nearby springs, and surrounding bedrock exposures.

Magnesium sulfate generally will precipitate sometime after or during precipitation of mirabilite but before precipitation of salt, precipitation more or less at temperatures less than 32 °C. Epsomite is generally considered as a cryophilic salt.

Bloedite (astrakanite $Na_2Mg(SO_4)_2 \cdot 4H_2O$) will precipitate from a pure water solution between $20°$ and $71 °C$ (PALACHE et al., 1951), but under lacustrine conditions where contamination of lake waters due to other ions occurs, the temperature is undoubtedly lowered. Bloedite, which can be considered a thermophilic salt, will crystallize from brines having an ionic composition similar to ocean water in the temperature range $4.5°–59.5 °C$. Because bloedite is essentially a mixture of sodium and magnesium sulfates, and because it is more or less in equilibrium with mirabilite and epsomite, most bloedite is associated with thenardite and mirabilite (EUGSTER and SMITH, 1965).

Bloedite deposits occur all over the world, the most interesting probably being in the Stassfurt, Germany, area (marine) and the interbedded bloedite–halite near Korduansk, Russia. In the United States bloedite occurs in several lake basins in California and New Mexico. Production of sodium sulfate from subterranean brines from sulfate deposits, undoubtedly with considerable bloedite, occurs at Rich, Brownfield, Cedar, and Monahans Lakes, Texas.

During a process of fractional crystallization, deposition of sodium carbonates occurs both before and after precipitation of sodium and magnesium sulfate. For instance, excess Ca^{2+} may appear as gaylussite and/or pirssonite before precipitation of thenardite (or mirabilite), but sodium carbonate ($NaCO_3$) will not precipitate

Fig.60. Aerial photo of the Salinas, Chihuahua, Mexico area, across the southeastern part (Franklin Bolson) of the pluvial Lake Palomas basin. Notice abandoned shorelines in lower left of picture and Salinas de Union salt producing facilities in center. The Sierra de Nariz are in the background and the Cretaceous outliers Cerro Almirez and Sierra de Nivertos stick out of the present playa. (Photo by courtesy of R. G. Ponsford.)

Fig.61. Glaubers salt (mirabilite) accumulating during the winter months, shore of Great Salt Lake, Utah. (Photo by R. E. Cohonour, by courtesy of Utah Geological Survey.)

until after halite, although the sodium carbonate will usually be contaminated by sodium sulfate and chloride.

The common alkaline carbonates, *natron* ($Na_2CO_3 \cdot 10H_2O$) and *trona* ($Na_2CO_3 \cdot NaHCO_3 \cdot 2H_2O$), are found in lakes in Nevada, Wyoming, California (Owens and Mono), and Utah in the United States and overseas in Egypt, South America, and central Europe. One of the world's largest trona deposits occurs in the lacustrine Green River Formation, Wyoming, at depths of about 1,300–1,600 ft. The trona, which covers at least 2,000 sq. miles and accounts for over two-thirds of domestic natural soda ash production, occurs in four beds, the thickest being about 10 ft.

OTHER SALTS

Other salts precipitated in closed lake basins include those of the borate, nitrate, and potash types. These salts are all of commercial value, potash and nitrates as agricultural chemicals and borax as a household and industrial chemical, but they generally fail to precipitate in most lake basins. In fact, scarcity of the borate, nitrate, and potash salts combined with the chemical associations revealed in existing deposits, indicates that all three precipitate only under extraordinary environmental and chemical conditions.

Borax ($Na_2B_4O_7 \cdot 10H_2O$) is found in many lakes in Tibet, South America, Kashmir, Chile, France, and Bolivia, and in California and Nevada in the western United States, but still must be considered rather rare. Searles Lake, California, produces about half the world's total and over 90% of the world's boron, the minerals *kernite* ($Na_2B_4O_7 \cdot 4H_2O$), borax, and *colemnite* ($Ca_2B_6O_{11} \cdot 5H_2O$) probably being the most important. The world's borate deposits are both lacustrine (Searles Lake) and marine (Stassfurt, Germany), the lacustrine deposits tending to be calcium borates and the marine deposits generally magnesium borates. This difference reflects the increase of the magnesium to calcium ratio between most lake and ocean waters.

Perhaps the best known occurrence of borax is the white crust which covers much of the playa of Death Valley, California (Fig.62). This is the crust which used to be mined and then transported by the famous "20-mule teams." Borax crystals generally tend to be equidimensional, but elongate crystals, such as those in Searles Lake, California, form from sulfate-rich waters with a pH < 9.7 (GARRET and ROSEN-BAUM, 1958).

Potash, used loosely for any salt rich in potassium, is perhaps the most soluble and consequently the rarest of all the lacustrine salts. Lacustrine potash salts and brines are known from California, Nevada, and Nebraska in the United States and overseas principally from the marine salt section, Stassfurt, Germany, area. Other nitrate areas of renown are in the Atacama and Tarapaca deserts of South America.

Fig.62. The salt encrusted playa of Death Valley, California, produced by repeated and continual thrusting of salt ridges. (Photo by R. W. Tall, by courtesy of National Park Service.)

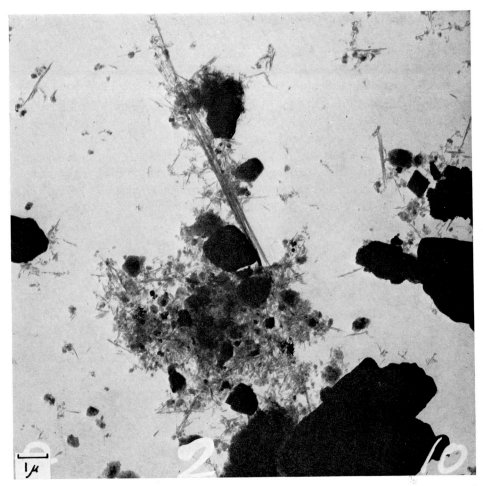

Fig.63. Transmission electron photomicrograph of clays from 2-ft. depth, Lake Mound, Lynn and Terry Counties, Texas. Long needles are sepiolite, opaque grains are kaolinite, illite, and montmorillonite clays. × 12.800. (Photo by John L. Brown.)

Potash is not generally produced from ancient lacustrine deposits, although the major sources of potash in the United States once were the small lake basins of the Nebraskan sand hills. Searles Lake, California, is the principal lacustrine source of potash today; but, production from ancient marine salt sequences as around Carlsbad, New Mexico, is commercially more feasible. Most subterranean lake brines do contain slight percentages of KCl but recovery is not profitable unless as a byproduct of another salt. Pluvial lake basins in West Texas contain, on the average, about 1–3 % KCl. Attempts to recover this small percentage, by solar evaporation, have been instituted by the Ozark–Mahoning Chemical Company at Cedar Lake, Texas.

Minerals such as sulfur, pyrite, marcasite, palygorskite, and sepiolite should also form in minor concentrations in hypersaline lacustrine environments (see

Chapter 8), but little is known of such occurrences. Sulfur nodules and palygorskite are known to occur in Lake Eyre, South Australia (BAAS-BECKING and KAPLAN, 1955), and marcasite, pyrite, and sepiolite occur (Fig.63) in some of the pluvial lake basins of West Texas (PARRY and REEVES, 1966).

Methods for calculating the age of the accumulation of salts in closed basins, based mainly on the Cl⁻ entering the basin, usually provide questionable if not grossly inaccurate results. The Cl⁻ entering any basin depends on the concentration in local rainfall, influents, and basin spring waters as well as amounts taken into solution by dissolving playa salts. Because the Cl⁻ concentration of each of the above depends on geographic location of the basin, prevailing wind direction, and regional and local lithology, it is nearly impossible to successfully utilize such methods. Peculiarities attendant such methods are well documented by BROECKER and WALTON (1959), FETH (1959), and LANGBEIN (1961).

Chapter 6

LACUSTRINE SEDIMENTS: CLASTIC

The types of lacustrine deposits, clastic, organic, or chemical precipitates, naturally depend on geographic location and the surrounding area. In areas of past continental glaciation, progression is usually from coarse clastics to the fine clastics to chemical precipitates, and finally to gyttja, peat, and sedge deposition. Mountain lakes exhibit principally coarse clastics, especially when above tree-line. Lake deposits in the periglacial areas generally do not contain much organic sediment, the clays, fine sands, and marls predominating. However, the amount of vegetation in a lake is certainly intimately related to the climate. For instance, the "bay lakes" of the Carolinas contain several feet of peat, yet at the same latitude peat is unknown in the pluvial lake basins of West Texas. Coarser clastics would theoretically be confined to nearshore or deltaic areas, silts and clays occurring throughout the lake basin. Thus, because deposition of the clastics is purely mechanical, their positions in ancient lake basins may be indicative of old shorelines or ancient drainage influents; the distribution, rather than lithology, may often be of most interest.

In the shallower parts of the old lakes, and particularly near influents where large deltas were possibly built, the lacustrine–fluvial stratigraphic relations became complex. During periods of lake desiccation fluvial sediments may have crept basinward as a clastic wedge, size of the clastics depending on size and competency of the influent. Likewise, during periods of lake expansion lacustrine sediments effectively buried deltas and even shore-fringing alluvial fans.

When a lake basin is surrounded by steep mountain fronts coarse debris is expected along the mountain front shore. This would be the normal case where alluvial fans might build lakeward, finally intersecting the lake, or the lake itself may actually bury existing fans, but in many instances the expected coarse alluvial slope gravels are conspicuously absent from the lacustrine facies. This peculiarity, as exists in much of the Tularosa Basin, New Mexico, and the Hueco Basin, Texas, is indicative of basin filling by fluvial or lacustrine debris rather than by alluvial fan aggradation from the surrounding mountains, a fact that is sometimes difficult for geologists not aware of limnological conditions to accept.

SILTS AND CLAYS

Silts and clays undoubtedly make up the greater per cent of clastic sediments in lake basins, many basins having hundreds, and some over 1,200 ft. of near-continuous lake clay (ALLISON, 1945). Naturally, nearshore the silts and clays are mixed with large clastics either brought to the basin by influents or eroded from the shoreline, but in the center of the lake the silts and clays are generally uncontaminated except by salt crystals.

Color of most lacustrine silts and clays ranges from white to black, gray-blue to green seemingly being predominant. White fine-grained sediments are produced by a high calcium carbonate content but, in most respects, are more correctly considered chemical precipitates. The pure, to near-white, fine-grained clays (clay size) of many of the West Texas pluvial lake basins belong to this category.

Black clays are produced by extremely high organic or sulfide contents, the older the sediments the greater the possibility for the sulfide. For instance, black clays in Wilcox Playa, Arizona, have little organic matter but a high sulfide content (A. Long, personal communication, 1967) while black clays in pluvial lake basins of West Texas, at least near surface, exhibit a low sulfide to organic ratio. With depth, sulfide to organic ratios generally increase. Exposures of ancient organic-rich lacustrine silts and clays will almost always be of light-colored grays to white, because of oxidation of the carbon. The exposed color in no way reflects what the unweathered color is, except suggesting a dark gray to black due to the organics.

Several terms such as *gel mud*, *sapropel*, *gyttja*, and *peat* distinguish different phases of fine-grained materials found in lake basins. For instance, gel mud, consisting of organically precipitated humic solutions, occurs before the development of sapropel, the black to gray anaerobically produced debris of closed lakes. However, if the environment is aerobic, both plant and animal debris contribute to the bottom sediment, developing gray to brown gyttja. Once the lake has nearly destroyed itself by filling, deposition becomes mainly organic, giving rise to a peat swamp or bog.

Present bogs, in a great many instances, mark old lake basins unless the bog has formed by accumulation of *Sphagnum* ("peat moss"). Naturally, bogs develop only in areas of abundant surface water and vegetation, *but* where growth of the vegetation exceeds decomposition. Thus, as the lake basins fill their water becomes continually shallower which allows shoreward vegetation to creep inward, restricting the area of open water. Soon the lake is completely breached by vegetation, the incomplete decomposition of which continues to fill in what remains of the marsh or swamp, the water becoming increasingly acidic (pH 3.5–6.0) and yellow to dark brown or black in color.

Exposures of green lacustrine silts and clays are common to ancient lake basins throughout the world. The green color, representative of a reducing environment, results from the presence of minerals with a high ferric iron content or perhaps by ferrous hydroxide ($Fe(OH)_2$), thus is indicative of "deep"[1] water conditions. There likewise seems to be a general absence of red silts and clays in most pluvial lake basins. The red color of typical "red beds" is usually caused by iron oxide or the presence of potassic feldspar fragments, thus absence of red lacustrine sediments from anaerobic environments is not unusual.

---

[1] "Deep" used in this respect refers to water depths exceeding the few inches common to playas.

In the pluvial lake basins of West Texas are some unusual green clays, dolomites, and sands, those of Lake Mound, Lynn and Terry Counties, Texas, providing an ideal area of study. Recent study (PARRY and REEVES, 1966) of the Lake Mound section shows the green coloration is due to authigenic glauconitic mica (Table IX). Additional detailed mineralogic studies of green lacustrine sediments may then be expected to show other like occurrences of glauconitic mica and perhaps even true lacustrine glauconite. The presence of green-colored lacustrine strata should no longer simply signify the presence of the ferric ion.

Mineralogically, lacustrine clays would theoretically consist of either kaolin, montmorillonite, or illite, depending mainly on climate in the source area and secondarily on environment of deposition and local geology. In many of the Pleistocene pluvial lake basins of the western United States montmorillonite is the predominant clay probably because of alteration of Pleistocene volcanic ash falls. However, both montmorillonite and illite form in basins surrounded by rocks rich in Mg^{2+}, Ca^{2+}, and Fe^{2+} providing stagnant (reducing) alkaline water conditions exist, illite forming under mild alkaline conditions, montmorillonite at high pH values. Lakes rich in previously stated cations would tend to be saline and exhibit evidence of lacustrine carbonates, thus lacustrine carbonates more or less indicate the association of montmorillonite and illite clays, which themselves suggest ancient, closed saline lakes and a semi-arid environment.

Kaolin clays are entirely different. Cations needed for the formation of montmorillonite and illite clays effectively block the formation of kaolinite, thus kaolin clays form in lake basins surrounded by rocks rich in alkali metals, usually at a pH less than 7.0. An oxidizing depositional environment is particularly required to convert the ever-present ferrous iron to ferric, although conversion to iron sulfide may suffice. Lacustrine kaolin clay is then indicative of a climatic situation where

TABLE IX

ANALYSIS OF MOUND LAKE GLAUCONITIC MICA

(After PARRY and REEVES, 1965)

Oxide	Weight $^o/_o$
SiO_2	41.6
Fe_2O_3	16.1
FeO	0.7
Al_2O_3	11.0
MgO	4.8
CaO	0.9
K_2O	3.8
Na_2O	3.3
H_2O (released $<115°$ C)	3.8
H_2O (released $>115°$ C) but $< 1,000°$ C)	12.7

precipitation exceeded evaporation so that the lakes were probably permanent and open. The possibility of the alteration of montmorillonite to kaolinite due to an increase in precipitation should always be investigated but is not likely.

Drainage as well as precipitation must also be considered. If precipitation exceeds evaporation, which would actually be expected to yield kaolinite clays (other requirements being equal), lakes may develop montmorillonite clays if they remain closed due to excessive seepage, which effectively allows accumulation of the required cations. The opposite condition could also exist if evaporation normally exceeded precipitation. Under such conditions a montmorillonite–illite association would be expected because of closed lakes, but if a lake gained an unordinary amount of water due to spring flowage, effluents could keep the cation levels sufficiently low to develop the kaolin clays.

Naturally the chemistry of the lake water is of tremendous importance in determining the type of clay which forms and, in fact, could probably produce clay types out of phase with surrounding rock types. Such should be the case of lakes immediately surrounded by alkaline-rich rocks which receive acidic influent waters due to flowage for much of their journey over acidic rocks. The importance of this consideration would depend on whether the majority of a lacustrine clay was originally formed in the soil of the surrounding basin or within the lake proper, an argument over which there is considerable debate (MILLOT, 1949; GRIM, 1953, 1958; WEAVER, 1958).

Fig.64. Sheet wash flooding the playa of Rich Lake, Terry County, Texas. The near-shore light colored band (arrows) is silt and clay that has been washed to the playa by runoff over the surrounding older lacustrine strata. The shoreline is marked by the dashed line. (Photo by the author.)

Study of pluvial lake clays shows a similarity to the clay type found in surrounding basin soils, analogous to clay minerals in a marine basin correlating with mineralogical character of the source area. However, certain horizons are often altered to a different clay type, obviously in response to climatic change. For instance, soils surrounding the pluvial lake basins of West Texas are rich in montmorillonite as are most of the upper parts of present lake fills. However, at a certain depth, dependent on the amount of playa deflation, the montmorillonite-rich lacustrine clays change abruptly to kaolinite-rich clays. This was undoubtedly caused by a change from oxidizing open lake conditions to the present stagnant, closed lake reducing conditions, due to a climatic change; however, the actual contact is disconformable and the hiatus represents an unknown amount of time.

The first considered source of fine-grained lacustrine clastics should be suspended debris brought to open basis by influents or to closed basins by sheetwash (Fig.64); however, in certain areas lake basins may have accumulated large quantities of glacial and/or non-glacial (FLINT, 1957) loess (Fig.113). Glacial loess accumulated mainly during the glacial periods when extensive outwash plains were forming, but desert (non-glacial) loess probably accumulated only during the dry inter-glacial periods. Thus, identification of loess in a lacustrine section could serve as a crude chronological tool.

SANDS AND GRAVELS

The lacustrine clastics larger than silt and clay may originate as: (*1*) a lag remaining after formation of a deflation basin, (*2*) fragments brought to the lake by influents, (*3*) fragments due to shore attrition, (*4*) fragments dropped by high winds or (*5*) fragments distributed by lacustrine currents. Such lacustrine clastics then seldom exceed boulder size, or about 10 inches.

Material due to wind transportation, outside of silt and clay, is mainly fine-grained sand and would be expected to be more or less evenly distributed over the lake basin providing basin size is or was not too large.

Size of clastics brought to lake basins by influents will depend on the competency of the stream, thus study of abandoned stream channels leading to pluvial basins lends considerable confidence to paleoclimatic projections, particularly when greater runoffs are suggested. Distribution of stream transported clastics usually is not extensive, so they tend to form small, coarse clastic wedges or lacustrine deltas. However, fluviatile gravels may sporadically exist in lake basin fills that represent alternation between a closed and open condition, the gravels generally being confined to a channel-like deposit surrounded by older lacustrine strata. Fluviatile gravels in West Texas pluvial lake basins which exist along the same drainage, are utilized as a correlative horizon between the basins.

In very large ancient lakes, or in large playas, longshore currents exist, due to wave action, which frequently cause distribution of course clastics along the particular lee shore. Islands near influents are especially favorable locations for intersecting and collecting influent clastics which are preserved as extremely clean gravel beaches (Fig.65).

Clastics produced by shore attrition depend on lithology of the shoreline and length of time of wave attrition. Angular sandstone fragments collect along some playa shorelines in West Texas pluvial lake basins because of erosion of Cretaceous outcrops, angular basalts and rounded carbonate boulders are accumulating along certain intermittent shorelines of the isolated playas of pluvial Lake Palomas, Mexico (REEVES, 1965), and lava beach pebbles once collected on the pluvial shoreline of Lake Nakuru, Africa (Fig.66).

The color of lacustrine sands and gravels varies considerably. As we have seen, some sands and gravels reflecting reducing conditions, are green due to authigenic glauconitic mica and perhaps glauconite (p.79), but most tend to have the predominant color of the majority of their fragments; clean quartz gravels or sands are white or gray while basalt fragments form a black sand or gravel. Contaminated or dirty sands and gravels tend to exhibit the color of their contaminating material, particularly as per cent contamination increases. Thus, most dirty lacustrine sands and gravels are shades of yellow-brown or red due to the iron oxides, and gray to black due to organic debris.

The thickness of lacustrine sands and gravels also depends on location. Sands tend to be more extensive than gravels, but are generally very thin. Gravels are perhaps more restricted aerially, as near a shore or at the mouth of an influent, but are usually thicker than the sands. Gravel sections 325 ft. thick are reported in Lake Bonneville sediments (FETH, 1955).

Because of the common presence of springs, fringing sand dunes, and sandy

Fig.65. Clean gravel beaches of Guzman playa, one of several remnant playas of pluvial Lake Palomas, Chihuahua, Mexico. Gravels were brought to the playa by the nearby Casa Grandes influent. (Photo by the author.)

Fig.66. Lava beach pebbles from old shoreline of (altitude of 6,383 ft.) Lake Nakuru, Kenya, Africa. (Photo by C. Washbourn.)

surface strata, playas frequently contain areas of quicksand. These quicksand areas usually appear during that part of the year when the local ground water table rises, disappearing during the dry summer months, but tending to reappear in the same location year after year. The lower area between a fringing lunette and associated playa, especially after an extended wet period, may be quick due to the playa, but this condition is usually obvious from the wet nature of the surface.

VOLCANIC ASH

Lake basins many hundreds of miles down wind from volcanic areas frequently collect volcanic debris, particularly the fine-grained siliceous ash (Fig.47). Such deposits undoubtedly occur throughout the world but are best known from the pluvial lake basins of the western United States (ALLISON, 1945; FRYE and LEONARD, 1957; EARDLEY and GVOSDETSKY, 1960; REEVES and PARRY, 1965).

Volcanic ash deposited in ancient lake basins usually presents a lenticular deposit, often with an irregular top. Thickness of most lacustrine ash falls is generally not great, but identification is often difficult.

Pleistocene ash falls are of particular interest to paleolimnologists since they usually are: (*1*) widely distributed, (*2*) good stratigraphic markers, and (*3*) may be dated by the potassium–argon method; however, ash is easily reworked, destroyed, and/or contaminated and therefore extremely difficult to work. Recent studies now suggest that different falls often have identical mineralogic characteristics, thus their use as definite stratigraphic markers is debatable.

The best known Pleistocene ash falls in the United States are the Mazama, the St. Helen's and Rainier, and the Glacier Park, all occurring in the Washington–Oregon–Idaho–Montana area. Unfortunately, throughout the classic Great Basin pluvial lake area, the only ash of consequence seems to be the Pearlette, or a Pearlette-like fall. The Pearlette supposedly occurred only in the Texas and Oklahoma panhandles and northeast throughout Kansas (Fig.67), but subsequent studies showed the existence of Pearlette or at least a Pearlette-like ash fall west of the supposed source of the Pearlette, the great Valle Grando of northern New Mexico.

The Pearlette, as a lacustrine deposit, is seldom over 9–10 ft. thick although some basins do have as much as 20–30 ft., perhaps due to reworking and redeposition of surrounding deposits. Age is considered Kansan, thus the numerous basins throughout West Texas, Oklahoma, and Kansas containing Pearlette Ash are considered of pre-Kansan age. Identification of the Pearlette, like other ash falls, is based on shard shape, index of refraction, color, and vesicles; thus, if an unknown ash exhibits different characteristics, it is not considered Pearlette. Unfortunately an ash which has the characteristics of the Pearlette may actually be Pearlette or simply represent

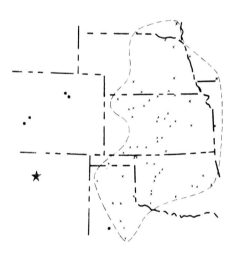

 ˣ Pearlette Ash

 • Pearlette-like ash

 ◌ Known area of Pearlette Ash fall

 ★ Valle Grande, long considered source of
      Pearlette Ash

Fig.67. Diagram of known area of Pearlette Ash of Kansan age. Five locations of ash closely resembling the Pearlette are shown in Colorado and West Texas. Other occurrences of Pearlette-like ash exist in Utah, Nevada, and Wyoming. The possibility that the Pearlette originated from the Valles Caldera as suggested by Swineford (1949) is now remote due to geographical distribution and mineralogy (Wilcox, 1965). (Modified after Swineford, 1949.)

a second fall of similar material. Correlation of ash falls from basin to basin is there-fore often conjectural, especially when variations in mineralogy may indicate minera-logic changes which occurred during ejection (THORARINSSON, 1954; WILCOX, 1954), dangers perhaps best illustrated by the Pearlette. SWINEFORD (1949), because of the then known distribution of the Pearlette and an understanding of paleowind directions, thought the source area for the Pearlette to have been northern New Mexico (Valles caldera), but recent discoveries of Pearlette-like ash in Nevada, Utah, Wyoming, and Colorado (RICHMOND, 1962) suggest either a different ash fall (SWINEFORD, 1963) or a more westerly source (WILCOX, 1965). YOUNG and POWERS (1960) suspect the Pearlette section consists of ash representing closely spaced multiple eruptions.

Age of volcanic ash falls can be accurately determined providing there is associated datable material, but unfortunately most ash falls, and particularly those of early and middle Pleistocene age, are not so associated. The discovery of a 22-ft. lacustrine deposit of Pearlette-like ash in West Texas (REEVES and PARRY, 1965), with four interbedded limestones (Fig.47), with radiocarbon dates ranging from 24,740 to over 37,000 years B.P., indicates that a Pearlette-like ash fall occurred during post-Kansan and probably Late Wisconsin time. Obviously then, age of any lake basin based on presence of Pearlette ash or, in fact, on the presumption of any volcanic ash, must be closely examined.

Chapter 7

LACUSTRINE STRUCTURES: DEPOSITIONAL AND EROSIONAL

The top of the lacustrine section located in the central low, flat part of an ancient lake basin, is generally termed the *playa* (Fig.68). The term playa, from the Spanish for shore, beach, has changed meaning, now referring in English to the central low, flat areas of desert intermontane basins. Correlative terms from other countries are listed in Table X. In the last few decades the term playa has been particularly and persistently applied to any dry lake basin located in the drier areas of the world, the so-called "playa lakes". Obviously it is not correct to speak of a dry lake basin as a "playa lake"; however, when the playa contains water the term is applicable.

Playas have been studied and classified by CLARKE (1924), FOSHAG (1926), THOMPSON (1929), JAEGER (1942), STONE (1956), SNYDER (1962), and MOTTS (1965), the

TABLE X

PLAYA TERMINOLOGY FROM SELECT AREAS OF THE WORLD

Country	Name
United States	playa (dry), salina (wet), alkali lake, salt lake, playa lake
Chile	salar (a lot of salt), salina (very little salt), tagarete (marshy area)
Southwest Africa	vlor (a dry lake), kalahari (a salt lake), kalkpfannen (a lime crusted playa)
North Africa	chott, sebcha, or sebka (a dry lake or the playa), merdja (a playa)
Arabia	sabkha, sabkaha (a salty playa), shott (a playa)
Iran	kewire (a dry lake, playa area), dariache (a short-lived desert lake)
Asia	nor, sabkehet, and schala (a dry lake, playa area), tsaka, tsidam (a salt lake or salt marsh)
India	rei (a dry lake. playa area)
Brazil	praia
France	plage
Russia	pljaž, pliazh (a playa), takyre (a dry lake)

Fig.68. Typical mud-cracked playa surface, Laguna Santa Maria, Chihuahua, Mexico. (Photo by the author.)

most recent detailed descriptions being those of STONE (1956) and NEAL (1965). CLARKE (1924) classified playas by the major salt content of the sediments, FOSHAG (1926) by whether the playa was wet or dry, and THOMPSON (1929) and JAEGER (1942) mainly by surface sediment, the result of a wet or dry situation. STONE (1956) bases his classification on whether the basin will or will not hold drainage. The simplest, most applicable classification for field use is division of the playa into either a wet or dry, smooth or rough type.

The principal characteristic of the playa is general smoothness and little slope, although protuberances such as old islands and lake depositional features commonly exist. The competency, and in fact even playa level, depends on elevation of the local water table: the lower the water the more competent the playa, yet the lower the probable elevation due to deflationary winds.

POLYGONAL PATTERNS

The most commonly observed features on playa surfaces are *mud cracks* (Fig.69) and *pressure ridges* (Fig.70), both of which form in polygonal patterns. The mud cracks result from desiccation and concomitant shrinkage of the playa sediments, their depth, length, and width apparently due to innumerable factors such as bedding thickness, salinity, foreign debris, gross lithology, rate of water loss, and position of the shoreline. Very wide and deep cracks, resulting from a declining piezometric surface causing deep-seated, long-term drying of fine-grained strata consisting pre-

Fig.69. Mudcracks preserved beneath 3 inches of water, Arch Lake, New Mexico. Notice ripple marks forming a playa surface. (Photo by the author.)

Fig.70. Pressure ridges formed by expansion of the salt crust of Lake Mound, Lynn and Terry Counties, Texas. Notice thrusting of one-half the ridge over the other half. (Photo by the author.)

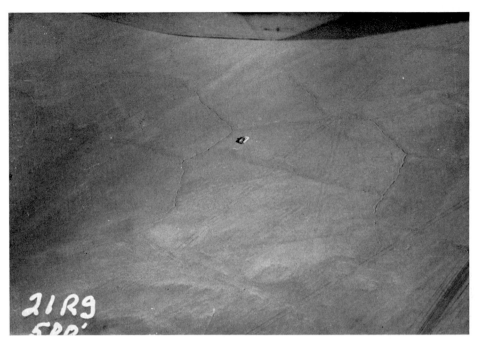

Fig.71. Contraction polygons at Rogers Lake, Edwards Air Force Base, California (1963). Altitude 500 ft. Distance across the polygons is about 350 ft. (Photo by U.S. Air Force, by courtesy of J. T. Neal.)

dominantly of clay and carbonates (NEAL, 1967), are termed contraction or desiccation polygons (Fig.71) or, when forming parallel lines, contraction stripes (NEAL, 1965a). Giant contraction polygons, often a meter wide, over 5 m deep, and 300 m across, were studied by NEAL (1965b) who finds formation occurring mainly on hard, dry, compact, desiccating playas underlain by a deep water table. Giant desiccation stripes, a variation of desiccation polygons, often form at right angles on long narrow playas or on narrow parts of large playas, the main factor controlling formations apparently being the stress field: stripes form in anisotropic fields, polygons in isotropic fields (NEAL, 1965c). Presence of both giant contraction polygons and giant desiccation stripes in old lacustrine sections may, therefore, be used as a qualitative paleoclimatic indicator; however, mud cracks, contraction polygons, and contraction stripes are not known to be specifically indicative of anything except drying, although NEAL (1965b) does suspect tectonic forces and subsidence of basins as possible contributory factors.

    Pressure ridges (Fig.70) form by expansion and growth of a salt crust, the more continuous crystallization is from a playa brine, the larger the ridges. The pressure ridges themselves may become over a foot in width and the polygons many tens of feet across. When crystallization occurs continually, year after year, the polygons soon thrust the salt ridges over one another, the overriding blocks (Fig.62) creating a highly irregular impassable surface.

MOUNDS AND DEPRESSIONS

   Spring mounds (Fig.72) result from escape of subterranean playa water, alignment of springs in many of the large intermontane playas of the western United
States indicative of deep-seated faults. In smaller basins springs often form along
mud cracks, especially when the subterranean water is under pressure. The topographic mound that forms around a playa spring is usually due to spring deposition,
either chemical or mechanical, associated with accumulation of deflated playa debris
on the wet spring area. The height of spring mounds then depends on the piezometric
surface and spring flow, too great an artesian head and flow tending to remove
rather than attract sediment. A large spring mound consisting mainly of deflated
debris may be indicative of a slowly rising piezometric surface but large spring
mounds consisting mainly of tufa, like those at Searles Lake or Mono Lake California (Fig.73), are obviously completely divorced from the local piezometric surface. Of course, spring mounds of tufa, sometimes termed "algal pinnacles", may be
of organic and/or inorganic origin. STONE (1956) reports artificial spring mounds
200–300 ft. in diameter at Rosamond Dry Lake, California, created by leakage
from abandoned water wells. The selenite buttes of STONE (1956) are probably
little different from spring mounds except perhaps flow of water is by capillary rise
rather than by spring conduit.
   Phreatophyte mounds (Fig.72) consist of deflated playa debris which collects
around the base of plants whose roots reach the water table (phreatophytes). The size

Fig.72. Incipient spring mound forming on playa of Guthrie Lake, Lynn County, Texas. Notice
young phreatophytes growing, the presence of which will act as collecting barriers for playa debris.
(Photo by the author).

Fig.73. Algal pinnacle, south shore, Mono Lake, California. (Photo by courtesy of D. W. Scholl.)

Fig.74. Playa sink forming due to lowering of the water table by the central phreatophyte, playa of Franklin bolson, Chihuahua, Mexico. (Photo by the author.)

of the mound is more or less determined by age and depth to which the plant root system can develop, thus certain plants may be indicative of maximum ground water table positions. Phreatophyte mounds over 10 ft. high occur at Big Smoky Playa, Blair Junction, Nevada (MOTTS, 1965). The genus and species of vegetation causing phreatophyte mounds on and around playas depends mainly on climate, depth of water, and quality of water (ROBINSON, 1958), the most common being saltcedar (*Tamarix gallica*), mesquite (*Prosopis*), greasewood (*Sarcobatus vermiculatus*), salt-grass (*Distichlis stricta*), and pickleweed or picklebush (*Allenrolfia occidentalis*). WHITE (1932) found the depth to the water table ranging from 3–50 ft. for greasewood, 4–15 ft. for saltgrass, and always less than 8 ft. for pickleweed.

Many playas exhibit *pseudo-phreatophyte mounds*, but these always have springs near their bases. The pseudo-phreatophyte mounds form primarily due to collection of deflation debris on the moist playa muds, vegetation taking hold around the spring. As the mound builds the seeping playa spring may be closed making it virtually impossible to recognize the true origin of the mound.

Playa sinks generally result from removal of water by phreatophytes (Fig.74) or by removal of saliferous sediments by percolating playa water or man-made injections or extraction of brine during salt-mining operations (Fig.75). Irregularly-shaped or very small sinks and slightly deformed beds are sometimes termed *slumps* (Fig.76) and small sinks are called *solution pits*. The decomposition of organic debris in lacustrine strata may produce enough gas (mainly methane) to effect escape by a small circular orifice termed a *gas pit* (MAXON, 1940). When gas escapes under water the agitation of the bubbles may produce a very large gas pit (Fig.77).

Spring pits (QUIRKE, 1930) form on and near sandy beaches due to escape of ground water. The pits, about 1–2 ft. wide, are crater-like with depths of about 6 inches, the rim being composed of fine-grained sand, coarser grains accumulating in the center of the pit. Although small spring pits have been observed along the playa fringes of the West Texas pluvial lake basins, they are not a common feature and, because of location and lithology, cannot be expected to be long preserved in the lacustrine sections.

Spring pots and *spring necks* (Fig.78) form from active spring flow in peripheral playa areas (REEVES, 1965). The spring flow carries the fine-grained and often easily dissolvable lacustrine sediment out toward the playa, creating a depression or "pot." Whether a spring neck forms depends mainly on flow of the spring and elevation of the spring above the playa. The greater the spring flow and the higher the spring above the playa, the more likely the formation of a spring neck. Spring pots are generally small, averaging only a few feet in diameter and a few feet deep; however, long continued flow well above playa level may form spring pots, such as at the south end of Lake Rich, Terry County, Texas, that are 30–40 ft. wide, 30–40 ft. deep, and connected to the playa by spring necks $\frac{1}{4}$–$\frac{1}{2}$ mile long.

Small concentric structures (Fig.79) formed on playas by escape of entrapped gas are termed *gas rings* (REEVES, 1964). Although gas rings could be quickly dismissed as spring pits or gas pits (Fig.77), close examination reveals that gas rings

Fig.75. Sinks produced on playa of Rich Lake, Terry County, Texas, by removal of underlying sodium sulfate by extraction of playa brines. (Photo by the author.)

Fig.76. Poorly sorted, near-shore lacustrine sand of Wisconsin age with interbeds of silt exposed on the flanks of Searles Valley, California. The slump structures shown in the left-central part of the photograph clearly occurred prior to deposition of the overlying relatively undeformed light-colored layer. The ruler is about 7 inches long. (Photo by U.S. Geological Survey, by courtesy of G. I. Smith.)

Fig.77. A very large gas pit formed in the Colorado River Delta, Lake Meade, Arizona. Grand Wash Cliffs in background. (Photo by W. Belknap, Jr., by courtesy of American Geological Institute.)

Fig.78. Three spring pots with short spring necks, southwest end of Lake Mound playa, Lynn and Terry Counties, Texas. Notice the utilization of one large spring neck. (Photo by the author.)

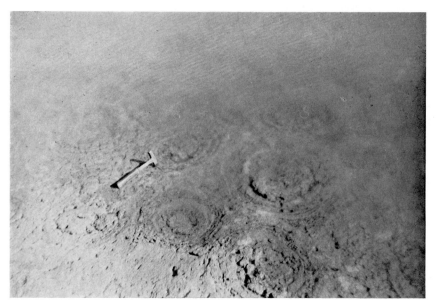

Fig.79. Gas rings, west side of Lake Rich, Terry County, Texas. Formed by entrapped air due to rapid playa filling which is forced upward due to slight seasonal rise of the water table. (Photo by the author.)

are formed by concentric circles of blow holes, often have a raised central area, form only under water, and are preserved in the section.

Gas pits have a single central, vertical vent, and apparently originate from greater volumes of more vigorously escaping gas than that which forms gas rings. Gas pits from 10 to 40 ft. long have been observed on some of the California playas (STONE, 1956).

Features such as salt "reefs" and salt "dikes", where local occurrences of relatively pure mineral occur in long tabular shapes, are sporadically found in larger paleolake basins. Origin of the "dikes" probably results from concentration in local fractures or fissures, the "reefs" representing along shore growth due to a wind driven wave supply, i.e., the sodium sulphate "reefs" of the Great Salt Lake shore.

ELONGATE FEATURES

Bars and *spits* form mainly in present large lakes, therefore, their remnants, or more recent shore features formed by modern periodic playa filling, can be expected in the larger paleolake basins. Both the bar and spit consist of sands, gravels, or sands and gravel deposited by wave action and longshore currents, the spit being attached to the shore at one end only. As long as the shoreline is relatively straight or even gently curving, longshore currents and direct wave action will deposit eroded debris as *shore-line bars* (Fig.80, 81), the lacustrine equivalent of marine barrier

Fig.80. Shoreline bars (arrows) formed between ridges of upturned Cretaceous limestone, by pluvial Lake Palomas, Chihuahua, Mexico. Age and elevation presently unknown. (Photo by the author.)

Fig.81. Shore-line bars (arrows), causing humps in road, in Ruby Valley (Lake Franklin), Nevada. View southwest to the Ruby Mountains. (Photo by U.S. Geological Survey, by courtesy of C. T. Snyder.)

Fig.82. The former 6,370 ft. shoreline of Lake Nakuru, Kenya, Africa, cut in unconsolidated pumice from the Meningai caldera immediately left of the picture. Lake level is now around 5,780 ft. (Photo by C. Washbourn.)

Fig.83. Shoreline of Level Post Bay, Lake Eyre, South Australia, during one of the rare times (October, 1950) the playa contains water, illustrating particularly fine development of pseudobars and pseudospits. Notice recurving starting to develop on ends of the pseudospits. (Photo by courtesy of C. Warren Bonython.)

beaches. When these shore-line bars extend in front of bays and irregular indentations they are termed *spits*. Ancient bars (Fig.80, 81) then exist lakeward of abandoned shorelines and more or less parallel the ancient beach, spits deviating from the beach and eventually terminating the bar. *Recurved spits* bend landward after extending lakeward for some distance, the spit becoming *cuspate* when it grows to join the shore. The presence of large lacustrine depositional features such as bars, spits, and beach ridges is indicative of vigorous wave action, thus these features will not be well developed in smaller lake basins or in lake basins that have held only shallow playa water. Poorly defined shoreline features (Fig.82), as now exist in the Lake Nakuru Basin, Africa (C. Washbourn, personal communication, 1967) then may be indicative of a past shallow lake, a small fetch, or great geologic age.

    Pseudobars or *pseudospits* may exist in intermittently filled lake basins due to transgression of landward sand dunes over the playa when dry. When the playa collects water the sand dunes, if not covered, may appear as normal bars and/or

Fig.84. Interbedded lake and alluvial deposits formed during Wisconsin time in Searles Valley, California. Deposits below the erosional unconformity (arrows) are mostly Middle Wisconsin in age, and those above are Late Wisconsin. The smooth surface is typical of sublacustrine erosional unconformities in this area, and contrasts with subaerial erosional unconformities which have more irregular surfaces. The dark bed just below the unconformity consists of a few inches of orange alluvial gravel, and along its top is a concentration of pebbles which probably represents a lag gravel formed by winnowing action of the lake or by subaerial deflation. (Photo by U.S. Geological Survey, by courtesy of G. I. Smith.)

spits. Of course the longer the water remains the more normal appearing become the pseudobars or pseudospits, spits being particularly susceptible to recurving. Pseudospits, pseudobars, and recent shoreline features are particularly well developed along the southern shoreline of Lake Eyre, South Australia (Fig.83).

Unconformities found in lacustrine strata (Fig.84) are due principally to fluctuations of lake level rather than to tectonic movements, therefore, extent of lacustrine unconformities tends to be a function of magnitude of water change and relief of the surrounding area. Obviously, a small rise in water depth in a flat deflation basin can cause extensive stratigraphic onlaps whereas a large rise in water depth in a karst basin may not greatly increase lake area. Of course, lacustrine unconformities are somewhat related to depositional rate in that if expansion of a lake occurs it is visually apparent only when deposition of lacustrine strata occurs. Since lacustrine unconformities are closely related to lake level fluctuations, the hiatus may represent very little time, although lacustrine unconformities produced by Pleistocene fluctuations are significant.

Because playas are seldom without any slope, due to depositional or tectonic influences, there always exists a lowermost part to which floodwaters first migrate. If an influent periodically contributes or directs large volumes of water to the playa, a channel or *playa groove* is cut in the playa surface (Fig.85).

The length of a playa groove depends on size of the playa and distance from the influent to the lowermost part of the playa. Depth and width of the groove are functions of the difference in elevation between the lowermost part of the playa and

Fig.85. The Salinas Groove cut on one of the present playas of pluvial Lake Palomas, Chihuahua, Mexico. This groove, though identifiable for only a few miles, directs the first playa flood waters to the Salinas area, the lowest part of the present basin. Width about 200–300 yards. (Photo by the author.)

Fig.86. The 50-mile long Warburton Groove, a playa groove which carries floodwater from the Warburton River to the lowest part of the playa of Lake Eyre, South Australia. Formation of the groove has apparently been due to slight tilting of the Eyre Basin to the south. (Photo by courtesy of C. Warren Bonython.)

the mouth of the influent as well as the volume of water contributed to the playa by the influent. Generally, playa groove cutting is offset by delta building so that good playa grooves more than a few hundreds yards long are difficult to find. The greatest playa groove known is the Warburton Groove which cuts 50 miles across the playa of Lake Eyre, South Australia (Fig.86).

The larger Pleistocene proglacial lakes of North America and Scandinavia rather consistently exhibit deformation of their shorelines, the result of isostatic rebound of the earth's crust caused by melting of glacial ice (BROECKER, 1966). Such uplift may cause regional truncation of lacustrine sections, producing a disconformable relation. Studies of crustal warping associated with proglacial lakes are most interested in extent of the uplift and strength and viscosity of the crustal layers rather than of the lake or basin itself. Recent study (SCHOLL et al., 1967) of Mono Lake, California, indicates that volcanic intrusions, sublake faulting, and basinward slumping of arched lacustrine strata have recently produced the topography beneath Mono Lake. Deformation of shorelines then must not necessarily always be delegated to isostatic rebound.

REFERENCES

ALDERMAN, A. R. and SKINNER, H. C. W., 1957. Dolomite sedimentation in the southeast of South Australia. *Am. J. Sci.*, 255: 561–567.

ALLISON, I. S., 1945. Pumice beds at Sumner Lake, Oregon. *Bull. Geol. Soc. Am.*, 56: 789–807.

ANDERSON, R. Y. and KIRKLAND, D. W., 1966. Intrabasin varve correlation. *Bull. Geol. Soc. Am.*, 77: 241–256.

ARMSTRONG, E. F. and MIALL, L. M., 1946. *Raw Materials from the Sea.*

ATKINS, W. R. G., 1930. Some geochemical applications of measurements of hydrogen ion concentration. *Sci. Proc. Roy. Dublin Soc.*, 19: 455.

BAAS-BECKING, L. G. M. and KAPLAN, I. R., 1956. The microbiological origin of the sulfur nodules of Lake Eyre. *Trans. Roy. Soc. Australia*, 79: 52–65.

BATEMAN, A. M., 1956. *Economic Mineral Deposits*, 2nd ed., Wiley, New York, N.Y., 916 pp.

BERKELEY, C., 1919. A study of marine bacteria, Straits of Georgia, B. C. *Roy. Soc. Can., Proc. Trans.*, 13: 15–43.

BERNER, R. A., 1965. Dolomitization of the mid-Pacific atolls. *Science*, 147: 1297–1299.

BIRGE, E. A., 1897. Plankton studies on Lake Mendota, 2. The crustacea from the plankton from July 1894 to December 1896. *Trans. Wisconsin Acad. Sci.*, 2: 274–448.

BIRGE, E. A., 1910. On the evidence for temperature seiches. *Trans. Wisconsin Acad. Sci.*, 16: 1005–1016.

BISSELL, H. J. and CHILINGAR, G. V., 1962. Evaporite type dolomite in salt flats of western Utah. *Sedimentology*, 1: 200–210.

BONYTHON, C. W., 1955. The weather record. In: *Lake Eyre, South Australia, The Great Flooding of 1949–1950*. Roy. Geograph., Soc. Australasia, Adelaide, 75 pp.

BONYTHON, C. W., 1956. The salt of Lake Eyre—its occurrence in Madigan Gulf and its possible origin. *Trans. Roy. Soc. S. Australia*, 79: 66–92.

BONYTHON, C. W. and KING, D., 1956. The occurrence of native sulphur at Lake Eyre. *Trans. Roy. Soc. S. Australia*, 79: 121–130.

BONYTHON, C. W. and MASON, B., 1953. The filling and drying of Lake Eyre. *Geograph. J.*, 119: 321–330.

BORCHERT, H. and MUIR, R. I., 1964. *Salt Deposits: the Origin, Metamorphism, and Deformation of Evaporites*. Van Nostrand, London, 338 pp.

BRADLEY, W. H., 1928. Algae reefs and oölites of the Green River Formation. *U.S., Geol. Surv., Profess. Papers*, 154: 203–233.

BRAITSCH, O., 1962. Entstehung und Stoffbestand der Salzlagerstätten. In: W. VON ENGELHARDT and J. ZEMANN (Herausgeber). *Mineralogie und Petrographie in Einzeldarstellungen*. Springer Berlin–Gottingen–Heidelberg.

BRAITSCH, O. 1963. The temperature of evaporite formation. In: A. E. M. NAIRN (Editor), *Problems in Palaeoclimatology*. Interscience, London, pp.479–490.

BRISCOE, H. T., 1951. *Chemistry*. Houghton Mifflin, New York, N.Y., 564 pp.

BROECKER, W. S., 1966. Glacial rebound and the deformation of the shorelines of proglacial lakes. *J. Geophys. Res.*, 71: 4777–4783.

BROECKER, W. S. and WALTON, A., 1959. Re-evaluation of the salt deposits chronology of several great basin lakes. *Bull. Geol. Soc. Am.*, 70: 601–618.

BREED, R. S., MURRAY, E. G. D. and SMITH, N. R., 1957. *Bergey's Manual of Determinative Bacteriology*. Williams and Wilkins, Baltimore, Md., 1094 pp.

BUCKLEY, H. E., 1951. *Crystal Growth*. Wiley, New York, N.Y., 571 pp.

CAMPBELL, L. L. and POSTGATE, J. R., 1965. Classification of the spore-forming sulfate-reducing bacteria. *Bacteriol. Rev.*, 29: 359–363.

CHILINGAR, G. V., 1955. Review of Soviet literature on petroleum source-rocks. *Bull. Am. Assoc. Petrol. Geologists*, 39: 764–767.

CHILINGAR, G. V., 1956. Use of Ca/Mg ratio in porosity studies. *Bull. Am. Assoc. Petrol. Geologists*, 40: 2489–2493.

CLARKE, F. W., 1924. The data of geochemistry. *U.S., Geol. Surv., Bull.*, 770: 841 pp.

CLARKE, G. L., 1939. The utilization of solar energy by aquatic organisms. *Publ. Am. Assoc. Advan. Sci.*, 10: 27–38.

CLOUD JR., P. E., 1962a. Behavior of calcium carbonate in sea water. *Geochim. Cosmochim. Acta*, 26: 867–884.

CLOUD JR., P. E., 1962b. Environment of calcium carbonate deposition west of Andros Island, Bahamas. *U.S., Geol. Surv., Profess. Papers*, 230: 138 pp.

CURTIS, R., EVANS, G., KINSMAN, D. J. J. and SHEARMAN, D. J., 1963. Association of dolomite and anhydrite in the Persian Gulf. *Nature*, 197: 679–680.

D'ANS, J., BUSSE, W. und FREUND, H. E., 1955. Über basiche Magnesium-Chloride. *Kali Steinsalz*, 8: 3–7.

DEER, W. A., ZUSSMAN, J. and HOWIE, R. A., 1962. *Rock-Forming Minerals*. Longmans, London, 5 vol., 1125 pp.

DEGENS, E. T., 1965. *Geochemistry of Sediments: a Brief Survey*. Prentice-Hall, Englewood Cliffs, N.J., 342 pp.

DEGENS, E. T. and EPSTEIN, S., 1964. Oxygen and carbon isotope ratios in co-existing calcites and dolomites from Recent and ancient sediments. *Geochim. Cosmochim. Acta*, 28: 23–44.

DEFFEYES, K. S., LUCIA, F. J. and WEYL, P. K., 1964. Dolomitization: observations on the Island of Bonaire, Netherlands Antilles. *Science*, 143: 678–679.

DUNBAR, C. O. and RODGERS, J., 1957. *Principles of Stratigraphy*. Wiley, New York, N.Y., 356 pp.

DUNN, J. R., 1953. The origin of the deposits of tufa in Mono Lake. *J. Sediment. Petrol.*, 23: 18–23.

EARDLEY, A. J., 1962. Glauber's salt bed west of Promontory Point, Great Salt Lake. *Utah, Geol. Mineral. Surv., Spec. Studies*, 1: 12 pp.

EARDLEY, A. J., GVOSDETSKY, V. and MARSELL, R. E., 1957. Hydrology of Lake Bonneville and sediments and soils of its basin. *Bull. Geol. Soc. Am.*, 68: 1141–1201.

EARDLEY, A. J. and GVOSDETSKY, V., 1960. Analysis of Pleistocene core from Great Salt Lake, Utah. *Bull. Geol. Soc. Am.*, 71: 1323–1344.

EUGSTER, H. P. and SMITH, G. I., 1965. Mineral equilibria in the Searles Lake evaporites, California. *J. Petrol.*, 6: 473–522.

FAIRBRIDGE, R. W., 1957. The dolomite question. In: R. J. LEBLANC and J. G. BREEDING (Editors), *Symposium on Regional Aspects of Carbonate Deposition—Soc. Econ. Paleontologists, Mineralogists, Spec. Publ.*, 5: 125–178.

FETH, J. H., 1955. Sedimentary features in the Lake Bonneville Group in the east shore area, near Ogden, Utah. In: *Tertiary and Quaternary Geology of the Eastern Bonneville Basin—Utah, Geol. Soc., Guidebook*, 2: 1–25.

FETH, J. H., 1959. Re-evaluation of the salt chronology of several great basin lakes: a discussion. *Bull. Geol. Soc. Am.*, 70: 637–640.

FLINT, R. F., 1957. *Glacial and Pleistocene Geology*. Wiley, New York, N.Y., 553 pp.

FOSHAG, W. F., 1926. Saline lakes of the Mojave Desert. *Econ. Geol.*, 21: 56–64.

FRIEDMAN, G. M., 1966. Occurrence and origin of Quaternary dolomite of Salt Flat, West Texas. *J. Sediment. Petrol.*, 36: 263–267.

FRITSCH, F. E., 1959. *The Structure and Reproduction of the Algae*. Cambridge Univ. Press, Cambridge, 1: 791 pp.; 2: 939 pp.

FRYE, J. C. and LEONARD, A. B., 1957. Studies of Cenozoic geology along eastern margin of Texas High Plains, Armstrong to Howard Counties. *Rept. Invest., Bur. Econ. Geol., Univ. Texas*, 32: 62 pp.

GARRELS, R. M., 1960. *Mineral Equilibria at Low Temperature and Pressure.* Harper, New York, N.Y., 254 pp.

GARRELS, R. M. and CHRIST, C. L., 1965. *Solutions, Minerals, and Equilibria.* Harper and Row, New York, N.Y., 450 pp.

GARRET, D. E. and ROSENBAUM, G. P., 1958. Laboratory studies on the crystallization of borax. *Am. Chem. Soc., 133rd Meeting, San Francisco, Calif., 1958,* P: 32 (abstract).

GRABAU, A. W., 1924. *Principles of Stratigraphy.* Dover, New York, N.Y., 1: 1185 pp.; 2: 581 pp.

GRAF, D. L. and GOLDSMITH, J. R., 1956. Some hydrothermal synthesis of dolomite and protodolomite. *J. Geol.,* 64: 173–186.

GRAF, D. L. and LAMAR, J. E., 1959. Properties of calcium and magnesium carbonates and their bearing on some uses of carbonate rocks. *Econ. Geol., 50th Ann. Vol.,* 1959: 639–713.

GRAF, D. L., EARDLEY, A. L. and SHIMP, N. F., 1961. A preliminary report on magnesium carbonate formation in glacial Lake Bonneville. *J. Geol.,* 69: 219–223.

GRIM, R. E., 1953. *Clay Mineralogy.* McGraw-Hill, New York, N.Y., 384 pp.

GRIM, R. E., 1958. Concept of diagenesis in argillaceous sediments. *Am. Assoc. Petrol. Geologists,* 42: 246–253.

HARBECK JR., G. E., KOHLER, M. A. and KOBERG, G. E., 1958. Water-loss investigations: Lake Mead studies. *U.S., Geol. Surv., Profess. Papers,* 298: 100 pp.

HAWES, G. H., 1881. On liquid carbon dioxide in smoky quartz. *Am. J. Sci.,* 21: 203–209.

HUTCHINSON, G. E., 1957. *A Treatise on Limnology.* Wiley, New York, N.Y., 1: 1015 pp.

HUTCHINSON, G. E. and LÖFFLER, H., 1956. The thermal classification of lakes. *Proc. Natl. Acad. Sci., U.S.,* 42: 84–86.

INGERSON, E., 1962. Problems of the geochemistry of sedimentary carbonate rocks. *Geochim. Cosmochim. Acta,* 26: 815–847.

JAEGER, F., 1942. Ein besonderer Seentypus: die Trockenseen oder Pfannen. *Geol. Meere Binnengew,* 6: 65–103.

JAMIESON, J. C., 1953. Phase equilibrium in the system calcite–aragonite. *J. Chem. Phys.,* 21: 1385–1390.

JOHNS, R. K. and LUDBROOK, N. H., 1962. Investigation of Lake Eyre. *Rept. Invest., Dept. Mines, S. Australia, Geol. Surv.,* 24: 104 pp.

JONES, B. F., 1965. The hydrology and mineralogy of Deep Springs Lake, Inyo County, California. *U.S., Geol. Surv., Profess. Papers,* 502-A: 56 pp.

JONES, J. C., 1914. The tufa deposits of the Salton Sink. In: D. T. MACDOUGAL (Editor), *The Salton Sea—Carnegie Inst. Wash., Publ.,* 193: 79–83.

JONES, J. C., 1925. The geologic history of Lake Lahontan. *Carnegie Inst. Wash., Publ.,* 352: 1–50.

JUNGE, C. E. and WERBY, R. T., 1958. The concentration of chloride, sodium, potassium, calcium, and sulfate in rain water over the United States. *J. Meterol.,* 15: 417–425.

KAZAKOV, A. V., TIKHOMIROVA, M. M. and PLOTNIKOVA, V. I., 1957. The system of carbonate equilibria (dolomite, magnesite). *Tr. Inst. Geol., Akad. Nauk, S.S.S.R., Ser. Geol.,* 64: 152 (in Russian); *Intern. Geol. Rev.,* 1 (1959): 1–39.

KELLERMAN, K. F. and SMITH, N. R., 1914. Bacterial precipitation of calcium carbonate. *J. Wash. Acad. Sci.,* 4: 400–402.

KRAUSKOPF, F. B., 1957. Separation of manganese from iron in sedimentary processes. *Geochim. Cosmochim. Acta,* 12: 61–84.

KRUMBEIN, W. C. and GARRELS, R. M., 1952. Origin and classification of chemical sediments in terms of pH and oxidation–reduction potentials. *J. Geol.,* 60: 1–33.

LA MER, V. K., 1952. Nucleation in phase transitions. *Ind. Eng. Chem.,* 44: 1270–1277.

LANGBEIN, W. B., 1961. Salinity and hydrology of closed lakes. *U.S., Geol. Surv., Profess. Papers,* 412: 20 pp.

LEIGHLY, J., 1942. Effects of the Great Lakes on the annual march of air temperature in their vicinity. *Mich. Acad. Sci.,* 27: 377–414.

MacDonald, G. J. F., 1956. Experimental determination of calcite–argonite equilibrium relations at elevated temperatures and pressures. *Am. Mineralogist*, 41: 744–756.

Marchandese, H., 1956. Contribution á l'étude des gisements de manganèse sédimentaire. *Intern. Geol. Conf., Manganese Symp.*, 1: 107–118.

Maxon, J. H., 1940. Gas pits in non-marine sediments. *J. Sediment. Petrol.*, 10: 142–145.

Millin, J. W., 1961. *Crystallization*. Butterworth, London, 268 pp.

Millot, G., 1949. Relations entre la constitution et la genèse des roches sédimentaires argileuses. *Géol. Appl. Prosp. Min.*, Univ. Nancy, II.

Millot, G., 1952. Prospecting of useful clays in relation with their condition of genesis. In: *Problems of Clay and Laterite Genesis—Am. Inst. Mining Engrs.*, 107–114.

Motts, W. S., 1965. Hydrologic types of playas and closed valleys and some relations of hydrology to playa geology. In: J. T. Neal (Editor), *Geology, Mineralogy, and Hydrology of the U.S. Playas—Air Force Res. Lab., Bedford, Mass., Environ. Res. Papers*, 96: 73–105.

Murray, J. and Irvine, R., 1889. On coral reefs and other carbonate of lime formations in modern seas. *Proc. Roy. Soc. Edinburgh*, 17: 79–109.

Neal, J. T. (Editor), 1965a. *Geology, Mineralogy, and Hydrology of U.S. Playas—Air Force Res. Lab., Bedford, Mass., Environ. Res. Papers*, 96: 176 pp.

Neal, J. T., 1965b. *Giant Desiccation Polygons of Great Basin Playas—Air Force Res. Lab., Bedford, Mass., Environ. Res. Papers*, 123: 30 pp.

Neal, J. T., 1965c. Giant desiccation stripes. *Geol. Soc. Am., Spec. Paper*, 87 (abstract).

Neal J. T., Langer, A. M. and Kerr, R. F., 1967. Giant desiccation polygons of Great Basin playas, in press.

Palache, C., Berman, M. and Frondel, P., 1951. *Dana's System of Mineralogy*. Wiley, New York, N.Y., 1: 834 pp.; 2: 1124 pp.

Parry, W. T. and Reeves Jr., C. C., 1966. Lacustrine glauconitic-mica from pluvial Lake Mound, Lynn and Terry Counties, Texas. *Am. Mineralogist*, 51: 229–235.

Passarge, S., 1904. *Die Kalahari*. Reiner, Berlin, 822 S.

Peterson, M. N. A., Bien, C. S. and Berner, R. A., 1963. Radiocarbon studies of Recent dolomite from Deep Spring Lake, California. *J. Geophys. Res.*, 68: 6493–6505.

Posnyak, E., 1940. Deposition of calcium sulfate from sea water. *Am. J. Sci.*, 238: 559–568.

Postgate, J. R. and Campbell, L. L., 1966. Classification of *Desulfovibrio* species, the nonsporulating sulfate-reducing bacteria. *Bacteriol. Rev.*, 30: 732–738.

Pytokowicy, R. M., 1964. *Rates of Organic Calcium Carbonate Nucleation*.

Quirke, T. T., 1930. Spring pits, sedimentation phenomena. *J. Geol.*, 38: 88–91.

Rankama, K. and Sahama, T. G., 1950. *Geochemistry*. Univ. Chicago Press, Chicago, Ill., 912 pp.

Reeves Jr., C. C., 1964. Gas rings from Terry County, Texas. *J, Sediment. Petrol.*, 34: 190–193.

Reeves Jr., C. C., 1965. Spring pots and spring necks, new geomorphic features from Lynn and Terry Counties, Texas. *Compass*, 43: 41–45.

Reeves Jr., C. C., 1967. Caliche. In: *Encyclopedia Earth Sciences*. Reinhold, New York, N.Y., 4: in press.

Reeves Jr., C. C. and Parry, W. T., 1965. Geology of West Texas pluvial lake carbonates. *Am. J. Sci.*, 263: 606–615.

Richmond, G. M., 1962. Quaternary stratigraphy of the La Sal Mountains, Utah. *U.S., Geol. Surv., Profess. Papers*, 324: 135 pp.

Robinson, T. W., 1958. Phreatophytes. *U.S., Geol. Surv., Water Supply Papers*, 1423: 84 pp.

Russell, J. C., 1887. Quaternary history of Mono Valley. *U.S., Geol. Surv., Ann. Rept.*, 8: 261–394.

Russell, J. C., 1893. A geologic reconnaissance in central Washington. *U.S., Geol. Surv., Bull.*, 108: 108 pp.

Ruttner, F., 1962. *Fundamentals of Limnology*. 3 ed. Transl. by D. G. Frey and F. E. J. Frey, Univ. Toronto Press, Toronto, Ont., 295 pp.

Scholl, D. W., 1960. Pleistocene algal pinnacles at Searles Lake, California. *J. Sediment. Petrol.*, 30: 414–431.

SCHOLL, D. W., VON HUENE, R., ST. AMAND, P. and RIDLON, J. B., 1967. Age and origin of topography beneath Mono Lake, a remnant Pleistocene lake, California. *Bull. Geol. Soc. Am.*, 78: 583–600.

SHAPIRO, J., 1956. *The Coloring Matter of Natural Waters*. Thesis, Yale Univ., New Haven, Conn. (unpublished).

SHINN, E. A., 1964. Recent dolomite, Sugarloaf Key: from south Florida carbonate sediments. *Geol. Soc. Am., Guidebook, Field Trip*, 1: 62–68.

SKINNER, H. C. W., 1963. Precipitation of calcium dolomites and magnesium calcites in the southeast of South Australia. *Am. J. Sci.*, 261: 449–472.

SMITH, G. I., 1966. Geology of Searles Lake—a guide to prospecting for buried continental salines. In: *Second Symposium on Salt*. Northern Ohio Geol. Soc., Cleveland, Ohio, 1: 167–180.

SNYDER, C. T., 1962. A hydrologic classification of valleys in the Great Basin, western U.S.A. *Intern. Assoc., Sci. Hydrol.*, 7: 53–59.

SNYDER, C. T., 1963. Hydrology of stock-water development in the Ely grazing district, Nevada. *U.S., Geol. Surv., Water Supply Papers*, 1475: 383–441.

STARKEY, R. L., 1935. Products of the oxidation of thiosulphate by bacteria in mineral media. *J. Gen. Physiol.*, 18: 325–349.

STONE, R. O., 1956. *A Geologic Investigation of Playa Lakes*. Thesis Univ. Southern California, Los Angeles, Calif., 302 pp. (unpublished).

STRAKHOV, N. M., 1953. Diagenesis of sediments and its significance for sedimentary ore formation. *Izv. Akad. Nauk. S.S.S.R.*, 5: 12–49.

SVERDRUP, H. U., JOHNSON, M. W. and FLEMING, R. H., 1942. *The Oceans: Their Physics, Chemistry, and General Biology*. Prentice-Hall, New York, N.Y., 1087 pp.

SWINEFORD, A., 1949. Source area of Great Plains Pleistocene volcanic ash. *J. Geol.*, 57: 307–311.

SWINEFORD, A., 1963. The Pearlette Ash as a stratigraphic marker. *Kansas Acad. Sci., Trans.*, 66: 358–362.

TERMIER, H. and TERMIER, G., 1963. *Erosion and Sedimentation*. Transl. by D. W. HUMPHRIES and E. E. HUMPHRIES. Van Nostrand, London, 433 pp.

THOMPSON, D. G., 1929. The Mojave Desert region, California. *U.S., Geol. Surv., Water Supply Papers*, 578: 759 pp.

THORARINSSON, S., 1954. The tephra-fall from Hekla on March 29, 1947, 2. The Eruption of Hekla, 1947–1948. *Reykjavik Visindafelag Islendinga*, 3: 68 pp.

THORP, J. and SMITH, H. T. U. (Editors), 1952. *Map of Pleistocene Eolian Deposits of the United States, Alaska, and Parts of Canada*. Geol. Soc. Am., New York, N.Y.

TWENHOFEL, W. H., 1950. *Principles of Sedimentation*. McGraw-Hill, New York, N.Y., 673 pp.

UREY, H. C., 1956. Regarding the early history of the earth's atmosphere. *Bull. Geol. Soc. Am.*, 67: 1125–1128.

USIGLIO, J., 1849. Analyse de l'eau de la Méditerranée sur les côtes de France. *Ann. Chem.*, 27: 92–191.

VAN HOOK, A., 1961. Crystallization, theory and practice. *Am. Chem. Soc. Monograph*, 152: 325 pp.

WEAVER, C. E., 1958. Origin and significance of clay minerals in sedimentary rocks. *Bull. Am. Assoc. Petrol. Geologists*, 42: 254–271.

WEBER, J. N., 1964. Carbon isotope ratios in dolostones: some implications concerning the genesis of secondary and primary dolostones. *Geochim. Cosmochim. Acta*, 28: 1257–1265.

WELLS, A. J., 1962. Recent dolomite in the Persian Gulf. *Nature*, 194: 274–275.

WEST, G. S., 1927. *A Treatise on the British Freshwater Algae*. Cambridge Univ. Press, Cambridge, Mass., 534 pp.

WHITE, W. N., 1932. A method of estimating groundwater supplies based on discharge by plants and evaporation from soil. *U.S., Geol. Surv., Water Supply Papers*, 659A: 105 pp.

WILCOX, R. E., 1954. Petrology of Paricutin Volcano, Mexico. *U.S., Geol. Surv., Bull.*, 965-C: 281–353.

WILCOX, R. E., 1965. Volcanic-ash chronology. In: H. E. WRIGHT, JR. and D. G. FREY (Editors), *The Quaternary of the United States*. Princeton Univ. Press, Princeton, N.J., pp.807–816.

WRIGHT, A. W., 1881. On the gaseous substance contained in the smoky quartz of Branchville, Conn. *Am. J. Sci.*, 21: 209–216.

YOUNG, E. J. and POWERS, H. A., 1960. Chevkinite in volcanic ash. *Am. Mineralogist*, 45: 875–881.

ZELLER, E. J. and WRAY, J. L., 1956. Factors influencing precipitation of calcium carbonate. *Bull. Am. Assoc. Petrol. Geologists*, 40: 140-152.

ZEN, E., 1960. Carbonate equilibria in the open ocean and their bearing on the interpretation of ancient carbonate rocks. *Geochim. Cosmochim. Acta*, 18: 57–71.

ZOBELL, C. E., 1964. *Marine Microbiology*. Chronic Botanica, Waltham, Mass., 240 pp.

Part III. The Paleolake Basin

JAMIESON (1863), over 100 years ago, suggested that many of the large closed lakes of Asia contained more water during the glacial, or "ice age," periods because of a decreased evaporation rate. At least part of Jamieson's idea was proven correct by LARTET's (1865) study of the Dead Sea. LARTET (1865) found abandoned high-level beach deposits associated with the Dead Sea and correctly assumed that they resulted from lake expansion during the same glacial period that scarred nearby Mt. Lebanon. As we have seen, the European studies were followed by GILBERT's (1890) and RUSSELL's (1885, 1889) works on Mono Lake, California, and Lake Bonneville, Utah. Today it is universally realized by all geologists that large lakes once existed in the closed basins of present arid to semi-arid areas of every continent, and that lakes in more temperate areas were, in many cases, at higher levels. Widespread evidence in the form of abandoned river terraces, abandoned drainage channels, rock drawings, abandoned sea beaches, fossils, and calcium carbonate cave deposits attest to the most recent Pleistocene climatic change. According to archaeological, geochemical, and geomorphological data, this last great change, the end of the last ice age, occurred about 11,500 years ago (ERICSON and WOLLIN, 1964).

Detailed studies of fluctuations of lakes in the Great Basin area of the United States have been made (HARDING, 1935, 1942; ANTEVS, 1938, 1948; HARDMAN and VENSTRÖM, 1941; LAWRENCE and LAWRENCE, 1961; MORRISON and FRYE, 1965; MORRISON, 1966), the most exact regional chronology determined perhaps for the Great Salt Lake (MORRISON and FRYE, 1965).

Unfortunately these studies have delineated the ancient lake levels but have not, as yet, revealed depths of the old lakes. The depth of an ancient lake cannot arbitrarily be assumed to have been simply the difference between the present playa and the highest recognizable shoreline, no more than can depth be assumed to have been from the base of the lacustrine section to the highest recognizable shoreline. Undoubtedly there may have been instances where some ancient lakes never contained more than shallow water, yet, likewise there were probably cases where many of the intermontane basins held perhaps thousands of feet of water.

Chapter 8

PLEISTOCENE CHRONOLOGY

Although the Pleistocene is popularly known as the Ice Age, glaciation has not been confined to only the last 1.5 million years of earth history. There is abundant evidence of Precambrian glaciation in South Africa, Greenland, Australia, Scandinavia, China, southeastern Canada, the Arctic, and India (KING, 1961; SCHWARZBACH, 1961a); of Mississippian glaciation in eastern Australia; of Permian glaciation in South Africa, central Africa, India, Australia, and South America (SCHOVE et al., 1958; KING, 1961) (Fig.87) and of Cretaceous glaciation in eastern Australia; thus different areas have, at various times, been caught in the grip of an ice age. The

Fig.87. Black areas represent distribution of glaciation during the Permian. (Modified from DUNBAR, 1960, by courtesy of John Wiley and Sons, New York, N.Y.)

occurrence of pluvial lakes throughout earth history, and the probable presence of their lacustrine sedimentary sections, is therefore strongly implied, although very little evidence of their pre-Pleistocene existence is known (see p.1). Unfortunately, little is known of the pre-Pleistocene or even of the Early Pleistocene glacial periods, our most complete knowledge being of the last (Wisconsin) glacial stage.

THE BOUNDARIES OF THE PLEISTOCENE

The Pliocene–Pleistocene boundary, prior to 1948, was generally loosely placed at the base of the first (Nebraskan) glacial advance, but there has been considerable interest in revision, not only of the Plio–Pleistocene boundary, but of all of post-Pleistocene terminology (BUTZER, 1964).

As established in the 1800's by DESNOYERS (1829), LYELL (1830–1833, 1839, 1873), and FORBES (1846), the post-Tertiary Period is divided into the Pleistocene and Recent Epochs of the Quaternary Period, yet from a time standpoint alone the Quaternary (1–2 million years) fails to match the extent of previous geologic periods. Presently it is suggested that the Plio–Pleistocene boundary be placed below the Villa-franchian of Europe which correlates with the Blancan of the United States (DURHAM et al., 1954), by fossils (ERICSON and WOLLIN, 1964), the appearance of the modern horse *Equus*, elephant *Archidiskodon*, cattle *Bos*, and climatic and tectonic consider-ations (BUTZER, 1964). Classically the Pleistocene includes all post-Pliocene strata, the Ice Ages of LYELL (1873), but with the exception of uppermost Recent or Holocene debris dating from about 11,000 years B.P. (BUTZER, 1964).

HUNT (1953) proposed that the Pleistocene–Recent boundary, at least in the Great Basin area, be placed at the end of the Altithermal (ANTEVS, 1948, 1952), the very dry period of about 7,500 to 3,000–4,000 years B.P. MORRISON (1965b) suggests using the top of the Toyeh Soil which has been recognized throughout the Great Basin as the Pleistocene–Recent boundary since the Toyeh was formed during late Altithermal time, is well-defined, mapable, and does not cross time lines. The author concurs with this usage.

DURATION OF THE PLEISTOCENE

Division of the Pleistocene in all areas of the world has long been based on four major periods of glacial advance, each separated by a major interglacial period (Table XI), yet there has been considerable disagreement as to time extent of any of the climatic periods. Fig.88 illustrates recent data on time extent of the various Pleistocene climates based on paleontology (ERICSON and WOLLIN, 1964). Notations as to chrono-logical positions of the various boundaries are also included in the right margin,

TABLE XI

GENERALIZED PLEISTOCENE TERMINOLOGY OF THE UNITED STATES AND EUROPE[1]

United States	Central Alps	Germany
Wisconsin	Wurm	Weichsel
Sangamon	Riss/Wurm	Eem
Illinoian	Riss	Saale
Yarmouth	Mindel/Riss	Elster/Saale
Kansan	Mindel	Elster
Aftonian	Gunz/Mindel	Weybourne/Elster
Nebraskan	Gunz	Weybourne

[1] Minor fluctuations are not indicated.

based on a 650-ft. core from Great Salt Lake (EARDLEY and GVOSDETSKY, 1960) and the solar radiation curves of MILANKOVITCH (1930). Terminology, as used in the United States, correlates with that of Europe as shown in Table XI.

The extent of Pleistocene time is still being thoroughly questioned (ERICSON et al., 1963, 1964; RIEDEL et al., 1963, EVERNDEN et al., 1964. EMILIANI (1958), by study of deep-sea cores, thought the Pleistocene occupied about 300,000 years,

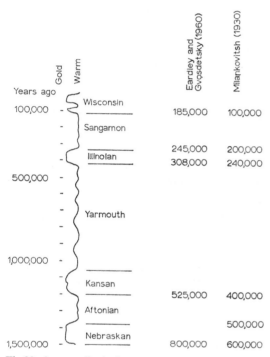

Fig.88. A generalized climate curve based on paleontology of deep-sea cores. (After ERICSON and WOLLIN, 1964.) The relative chronological positions of the major Pleistocene boundaries, as determined by study of a core from the Great Salt Lake, Utah, and from study of solar radiation curves, are indicated to illustrate the wide discrepancies which exist.

MILANKOVITCH (1930) and ZEUNER (1950) about 600,000 years from study of solar radiation cycles, and EARDLEY and GVOSDETSKY (1960) about 800,000 years from study of a core from the Bonneville Basin. HOLMES (1960) suggested about 1 million years but recently ERICSON et al. (1964), by extrapolation from deep-sea cores, project the Plio–Pleistocene boundary to 1.5 million years B.P., and BUTZER (1964) suggests 2 million years B.P. These lengthier dates are more or less substantiated by EVERNDEN et al. (1964) who dated a Kansan-aged volcanic at 1 million years and a Late Blancan range from 1.5 to 3.3 million years. Fig.88 shows a few of the various Pleistocene time scales.

PLEISTOCENE CHRONOLOGY

Generalized Pleistocene chronology, especially of post-Wisconsin time and particularly of the immediate pre-Recent, is more or less well known and universally accepted. Although several differences exist when attempting to correlate short-term local environments, lake basin sediments throughout the world clearly and synchronously exhibit evidence of the major post-Wisconsin climatic changes.

The most recent glacial maximum occurred perhaps about 22,000 to 18,000 years B.P., glacial melting apparently beginning in earnest about 19,000 years B.P. The exact date when glacial melting began is unknown but would be expected to have been different from area to area. Evidence from glaciated North America suggests that rapid retreat of the glaciers began about 18,000 years B.P. (FLINT, 1955) and recent studies of eustatic sea level changes (Fig.89) suggest a rapid rise beginning about 18,500 years B.P. (McFARLAN, 1961), a correlation of remarkable significance. Studies of oceanic sediments (EMILIANI, 1955a; ERICSON, et al., 1956) suggest dates ranging from 16,500 to 11,000 years B.P.

Evidence from lacustrine sediments, at least from the western United States and Europe, is indicative of a severe period of desiccation (OLDFIELD and SCHOENWETTER, 1964; REEVES, 1966) occurring about 18,000–17,000 years B.P.; however, pluvial conditions were apparently soon restored and it was not until about 12,000 years B.P. (Two Creeks interstadial time) that a serious change in ocean temperature occurred (EWING and DONN, 1956; BROECKER et al., 1960).

From about 12,000 to 7,500 years B.P. there exists evidence of increasingly warmer and drier conditions, culminating in the beginning of the Altithermal or "thermal maximum" of FLINT and DEEVEY (1951) about 7,000–6,000 years B.P.

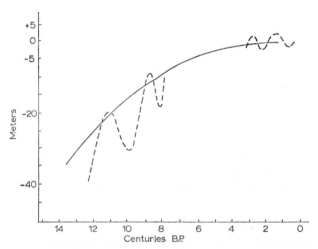

Fig.89. Ocean level from about 15,000 years B.P. to the present, the 15,000 to 7,000 year part due mainly to Wisconsin glaciers in the northern hemisphere, the 7,000 to present part due to Antarctic ice. The solid line represents the general eustatic rise, the dashed line several known oscillations. (After BLOCH, 1965.)

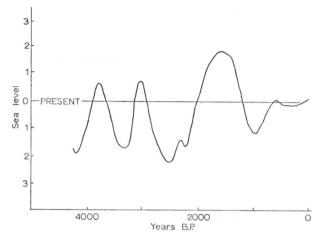

Fig.90. Estimated sea level changes during the last 5,000 years based on available historic data. (After BLOCH, 1965.)

It was about this time that the world's oceans reached their present level (Fig.90). The Altithermal, evidence of which exists in such widespread areas as Australia (BROWNE, 1945; FAIRBRIDGE, 1948), the Pacific Ocean basin (STEARNS, 1941, 1945a, 1945b), Africa (CATON-THOMPSON and GARDNER, 1929, 1932), and West Texas (REEVES, 1966a, 1966b; PARRY and REEVES, 1967) was finally broken by amelioration of the climate 4,000–3,000 years B.P. Climatic changes during the last 4,000 years or so, which have included several small "ice ages", have generally been of such small scale that they are best recorded by bog deposits (DEEVEY, 1958). Evidence for these major climatic changes exists in the larger paleolake basins throughout the world.

HYPOTHESES ABOUT THE CAUSE OF THE PLEISTOCENE ICE AGES

The definite cause (or causes?) of the Pleistocene ice ages, or any other world-wide period of glaciation, is not known with any certainty, nor does there even seem to be one cause more scientifically correct than the others. Basically glaciers develop when: (1) there is sufficient moisture for precipitation, (2) the temperature is below freezing, and (3) winter snowfalls exceed summer melting; however, SCHAEFER (1950) suggests that condensation of atmospheric water vapor requires nuclei, both SCHAEFER (1950) and MENZEL (1953) believing volcanic dust the most likely source. Not only is the source of Pleistocene atmospheric nuclei unknown, but whether increased precipitation or lower summer temperature is the most important factor for stimulation of glacial growth is highly conjectual, for considerable evidence supporting both possibilities exists (CHEMEKOV, 1960; LAMB, 1964; DONN and EWING, 1966). Nevertheless, of most interest is the reason behind the increased precipitation and for the lower summer temperatures.

The following resume summarizes some of the more interesting hypotheses regarding the cause of the Pleistocene ice ages and supplies references for those wishing to pursue the subject in greater detail:

(1) Ice-free Arctic Ocean. The ice-free Arctic Ocean causes precipitation over the northern continental areas which accumulates as snow and then glaciers. When ocean level drops below shallow shelfs, interchange of warm water from the Atlantic and Pacific oceans stops, and Arctic waters cool and freeze. This stops precipitation and glaciers wane. (See EWING and DONN, 1956, 1958.)

(2) Continental uplifts—tectonic–isostatic changes. Reduction of interchange of Atlantic and Pacific ocean waters into Arctic Ocean by tectonic–isostatic movement of a sill, and continental position in the northern latitudes, causes glaciation. Melting occurs because of lack of precipitation in northern latitudes. Isostatic rebound initiates a new glacial period by simple reduction of temperature. (See TANNER, 1965). Uplifts or expansion of continental areas by mountain building (EMILIANI and GEISS, 1959) may initiate glaciation because of temperature decreases, changes in circulation, and/or self-induced cooling by the snow and ice. (See DANA, 1856; RAMSAY, 1910; BROOKS, 1949a, and EMILIANI, 1958.)

(3) Ocean cooling. Study of oxygen isotope ratios of belemnites and foraminifera and paleofloras shows a general cooling of the oceans since the Cretaceous, perhaps caused by a general overall cooling of the earth. (See UREY, et al., 1951; ÖPIK, 1953; EMILIANI, 1954b, 1955b; and SCHWARZBACH, 1963.)

(4) Polar wandering and/or continental drift. Climatic changes caused by variable positions of the polar areas. (See SCHWINNIR, 1936; GOLD, 1955; and BROUWER, 1953.) DONN and EWING (1966), in a continuation of their ice-free Arctic Ocean theory, suggest migration of earth's poles to geographic regions of thermal isolation as the critical method of initiating glaciation: actual movement of continental masses. (See KÖPPEN and WEGENER, 1924; RUNCORN, 1956, 1962; HOWELL and MARTINEZ, 1957; DOELL and COX, 1961; OPDYKE, 1962; MUNK and MARKOWITZ, 1960.)

(5) Orbital changes. Solar radiation curves determined from earth's eccentric orbit (period of about 92,000 years), inclination of the axis (period of about 40,000–41,000 years), and westward movement of the equinoxes (period of about 21,000 years), indicate possibility of glaciation occurring after a decrease in radiation, melting beginning after an increase in radiation (MILANKOVITCH, 1938, 1941). (Also see CROLL, 1875; BRÜCKNER, 1890; KÖPPEN and WEGENER, 1924; BELL, 1953; VAN WOERKOM, 1953; KARLSTROM, 1961; and ZEUNER, 1959, 1961).

BROECKER (1966), comparing insolation changes to absolute dates (protactinium 231/ionium 230), shows that glacial periods developed in response to insolation changes due to periodic movements in tilt and precession of earth's axis. A decrease in obliquity of the axis, and a reduction of the ratio of the mean distance minus the summer distance of the earth from the sun, is divided by the mean distance, producing cold summers (VAN WOERKOM, 1953; BROECKER, 1966).

Glaciation may have been caused by reduction of temperatures due to sun spots, satellite shadows, and/or variability of the sun's radiation. Recent studies on

Alaskan glaciers (M. M. MILLER, 1967) suggest a definite correlation for the last 200 years between number of sunspots and world climate, the weather becoming colder and wetter as the number of sunspots decrease. The occurrence of sunspot cycles of approximately 11, 23, and 21,000 years is well documented from varve studies of Precambrian to Recent strata (KORN, 1938a, b; ANTEVS, 1925; WOLBACK, 1953). (See DUBOIS, 1893; HUNTINGTON and VISKER, 1922; SIMPSON, 1934; IVES, 1940; THORARINSSON, 1940; HIMPEL, 1947; WILLETT, 1949, 1953, 1961, 1964; LAWRENCE, 1950; ÖPIK, 1950, 1953, 1958a; SHAPLEY, 1953; and KROOK, 1953; for additional details.)

(6) *Oceanic salts.* Increase in oceanic salinity in equatorial areas supposedly caused rapid southward flow of fresher, but colder Arctic Ocean water which lowered earth temperatures. (See CHAMBERLIN, 1899; KRAUS, 1961.)

(7) *Volcanic activity.* Submarine volcanic activity caused increased evaporation, increased cloudiness, and hence glaciation. Volcanic ash due to excessive volcanic activity also may have decreased solar radiation. (See KRIGE, 1929; FUCHS and PATTERSON, 1947; WEXLER, 1952, 1960; and MITCHELL, 1961.)

(8) *Atmospheric H_2O and CO_2 changes.* Lowering of the CO_2, perhaps caused by increase of atmospheric water vapor (clouds), reduced solar radiation which caused glaciation. (See PLASS, 1956, 1961; and WEXLER, 1953.)

Another possibility is based on unnatural cooling of only one polar region which causes warm, moist equatorial air to invade the polar area where condensation allows building of the glaciers (QUINN, 1966).

This list of references to possible causes of the ice ages is far from exhaustive, yet does present some of the more interesting if not important of the various hypotheses. SCHWARZBACH (1963) mentions that over 50 possible causes have been suggested, none of which appears wholly acceptable, thus as MENZEL (1953) earlier wrote, there is a problem in itself created simply by the unusually large number of available hypotheses. Interested readers should not fail to review FAIRBRIDGE (1961c) on this general subject.

Chapter 9

DISTRIBUTION, CAUSE, AND RECOGNITION OF PALEOLAKES

Studies of pluvial lake fluctuations, of the origins of pluvial lake basins, and of pluvial paleoclimatic parameters, have been underway in most areas of the world. The studies shown in Table XII are some of those dealing with pluvial lakes and Pleistocene climates in countries other than the United States; obviously the list is very incomplete, but does give an indication of the interest accorded paleolimnology.

TABLE XII

GENERALIZED AND GREATLY ABBREVIATED LIST OF PLEISTOCENE LAKE STUDIES OTHER THAN THOSE IN THE UNITED STATES

Country	Investigator and year
Africa	BEADNELL (1909), LEAKEY (1930), NILSSON (1931, 1938, 1940, 1953), CATON-THOMPSON and GARDNER (1934), WAYLAND (1934), QUEZEL and MARTINIZ (1961), GROVE and PULLAN (1963).
Australia	DAVID (1932, 1950), BONYTHON and MASON (1953), BONYTHON (1955, 1956, 1958, 1960, 1961, 1963), GALLOWAY (1965, 1966), BOWLER and HARFORD (1966), MANN (1966).
China	PUMPELLY (1905), HUNTINGTON (1907), CARRUTHERS (1914), PENCK (1931).
Mexico	JAEGER (1926), DEEVEY (1944), SEARS (1952), SEARS and CLISBY (1955), FOREMAN (1955), REEVES (1965b).
Mid-East	HUNTINGTON (1914), BLANCKERHORN (1912,1921–1922), GERASIMOV (1930), PENCK (1936), BOBEK (1937), GRAHMANN (1937), LOUIS (1938).
Russia	PUMPELLY (1905), PRINZ (1909).
Tibet	HUNTINGTON (1906), HUTCHINSON (1939).
Europe	POSER (1951), FRENZEL and TROLL (1952), TRICART (1956a), KAISER (1960), ANDERSON (1961), WRIGHT (1961).
Ireland	LOUIS (1934).

DISTRIBUTION OF PALEOLAKES

The generalized extent of pluvial lake basins in the western United States, the southern High Plains, and northern Mexico, is shown in Fig.91. Unfortunately most of the basins have never been studied in any detail, nor have their playas been drilled to reveal the lacustrine section, thus the Pleistocene chronology of the western United States has been deduced and interpolated mainly from work in the Lake Bonneville and Lake Lahontan basins. However, comparison of Lake Bonneville's size (280 miles long, 140 miles wide, 20,000 square miles) to available data emphasizes that detailed geologic knowledge is lacking. Fortunately, near-continuous cores of the lacustrine sections have been secured and studied from Lake Bonneville (BROECKER and ORR, 1958; EARDLEY and GVOSDETSKY, 1960; BROECKER and KAUFMAN, 1965) and Searles Lake, California (SMITH and HAINES, 1964; STUIVER, 1964), allowing interpolation of geologic history of two of the most important pluvial basins in North America.

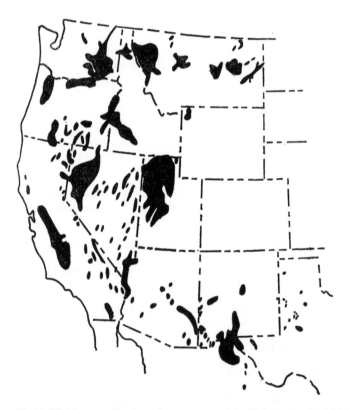

Fig.91. Highly generalized maximum extent of the Pleistocene pluvial lakes of western United States and Northern Chihuahua, Mexico. For the larger basins, as in western Nevada and around El Paso, Texas, only the most general outline is used: no islands are indicated and only major changes in the shoreline are shown. (Modified after FETH, 1964.)

CAUSES OF PALEOLAKES

A great deal of controversy exists as to whether the glacial periods were actually colder and wetter than the interglacial periods (CHARLESWORTH, 1957); QUINN (1966), in fact, suggesting that the whole idea is ". . . incompatible with the gas laws." AM-BROGGI (1966) reports that studies by Bernard of the earth's orbit, eccentricity, and position of perihelion reveal that the Sahara Desert, Africa, received the greatest amounts of Pleistocene rainfall during interglacial periods, results also supported by occurrence of fossil sand dunes in Africa (FAIRBRIDGE, 1961a). In the Southern Hemisphere the last Australian glacial climate was supposedly characterized by dry windy conditions (GALLOWAY, 1965, 1966), the formation of lakes due to a drastic reduction in evaporation. The post-Glacial Australian climate during the Altithermal phase of the Northern Hemisphere, at least in northern Victoria and southern New South Wales, also allowed formation of extensive lakes and associated drainage, windy conditions indicated by numerous lunettes (BOWLER and HARFORD, 1965). It is interesting to note, however, that studies of Recent hydrologic changes in glaciers and lakes in the Northern and Southern Hemisphere indicate penecontemporaneous environmental changes (LAWRENCE and LAWRENCE, 1965, and LAWRENCE, 1966).

RECOGNITION OF PALEOLAKES

MEINZER (1922) long ago suggested that the size of a pluvial lake depended on altitude, topography, relief, size of drainage basin, bedrock condition, and climate, but as SNYDER (1967) points out, only climate was subjected to significant short-term changes. Thus, the primary reason basins in present semi-arid to arid areas of the world contained water during pluvial (glacial) times was due to the drastic change in the weather, and not simply because of glacial melt waters. Certainly basins sur-rounded by mountains high enough to have supported Pleistocene glaciers received melt water, but the greater per cent of the increased water regimen was due to a southern shift of the westerly storm belt.

Climatic changes

Climatic changes that occurred during Pleistocene time were, of course, of world-wide extent, so let us now examine world atmospheric conditions.

The distribution of air masses over the world, for both the Northern and Southern Hemispheres, is basically tricellular (PFELLER, 1964), thus during any of the Pleistocene Ice ages three predominant climatic belts also must have existed, parti-cularly over the continental areas of the Northern Hemisphere. The first, and perhaps the climatic belt of most interest, was that existing mainly over the ice mass. The second extended over the peripheral areas and a third over the relatively uneffected equatorial areas. Boundaries between the three climatic zones were, of course, gradational with the sharpest change occurring between the ice sheet-peripheral or periglacial zones. Because of the cold temperatures and high barometric pressures a semi-permanent high existed over the ice sheet which must have squeezed the prevailing westerly storm belt southward over the periglacial or Great American Desert area (PENCK, 1914; KEBLE, 1947; BÜDEL, 1949; EWING and DONN, 1956, 1958; FAIRBRIDGE, 1964), the steady equatorial belt preventing too great a southward movement. The exact displacement is unknown but seems to have been from 3 to perhaps 15 or even 20 degrees of latitude (PENCK, 1914; EWING and DONN, 1956, 1958, 1961; CHARLESWORTH, 1957; FLINT, 1957; BUTZER, 1964). The storm belt, with its wet, cloudy air, drastically lowered the evaporation rate, but whether precipitation actually increased is conjectural and certainly was dependent on local conditions, just as precipitation is controlled today. Certainly the amount of available surface water (runoff) increased and temperatures were perhaps at least $10°$ cooler simply because of cloud cover (MITCHELL, 1965). Studies from various pluvial lake areas throughout the world show, for instance, an increase in pluvial precipitation in the American southwest (LEOPOLD, 1951; CARLSTON, 1963; MEHRINGER and HAYNES, 1965; M. A. MELTON, 1965; TANNER, 1965; REEVES, 1966b), a decrease in Australia (GALLOWAY, 1965), a 50% increase in central Europe, and no great change in the Middle East (BOBEK, 1937, 1964).

CHARLESWORTH (1957) states that "Precipitation is without question indispensable to glacierisation," but it is unclear whether glacial-age precipitation was less than, the same as, or greater than today's precipitation. In glaciated areas Pleistocene snow lines (Table XIII) are only about half as low as they should have been based on calculated lowering of the temperature (SCHWARZBACH, 1963), yet in present mid-latitude semi-arid to arid areas glacial precipitation was obviously much greater, giving the pluvial or rain climates. Therefore, the amount of precipitation over glaciated areas is unknown, and may well have been even lower than today's figure (SCHWARZBACH, 1963). However, Pleistocene lake terraces of pluvial lakes in the Great Basin, Mexico, Australia, East Africa, as well as the elevated beaches along the shores of the Aral, Caspian, Black, and Dead Seas, and the great abandoned wadis of the Sahara, vividly emphasize at least the local *surpluses* of precipitation over evaporation that existed in certain Pleistocene climatic belts. Estimates of the increase in precipitation necessary to sustain several pluvial lakes in the southwestern United States range from about 10 to 20 inches (LEOPOLD, 1951; ANTEVS, 1952; BROECKER and ORR, 1958; SNYDER and LANGBEIN, 1962; REEVES, 1966b). The exact pluvial relations between precipitation, evaporation, and runoff obviously differed from one area to another, but present environmental conditions generally establish, for the pluvial lake areas, a maximum (pluvial) for evaporation and a minimum for precipitation and runoff.

The equatorial shift of the westerly storm belt was worldwide (PENCK, 1914), and apparently took place in both hemispheres, thereby causing a general squeezing of the climatic zones near the equator, yet in some areas, as on the Australian continent, the desert belt apparently spread (GALLOWAY, 1965). Whether the deserts contracted or spread during glacial times is again probably a question of local variables, but at

TABLE XIII

DEPRESSION OF PLEISTOCENE SNOW LINE

Author	Location	Feet
Butzer (1964)	Appennine Mountains	>3,608
Butzer (1964)	Cantabrian Mountains	3,280
Butzer (1964)	Morocco Rif Mountains	3,280
Butzer (1964)	North Iran	2,296–2,624
Charlesworth (1957)	Alps	4,280
Flint (1937)	Sierra Nevadas	4,264
Flint (1957)	Mt. Kilimanjaro	4,280
Klute (1921)	Front Range	3,280
Klute (1928)	Arctic	1,960
Louis (1934)	British Isles	3,940
Penck (1914)	Asia	3,300–4,600
Penck (1914)	Caucasus	4,300
Penck (1914)	Japanese Alps	>3,300
Penck (1914)	Mediterranean	3,300–4,000
Penck (1914)	Mt. Kenya	>4,000
Penck (1914)	Pyrenees	>3,300 (west)
Richmond (1965)	Rocky Mountains	4,000
Schwarzbach (1963)	Alps Mountains	3,940
Stearns (1942)	New Mexico	4,750
Wilhelmy (1957)	Andes Mountains	4,580

least we can definitely state that the deserts of both hemispheres were not destroyed by pluvial periods. The northern Sahara, Africa, has experienced heavy runoff which built great alluvial fans, created extensive lakes, and supported a Mediterranean-type flora at sometime in the Pleistocene, while to the south the great deserts of South Africa, the Karroo and Kalahari, have had permanent streams. Evidence for a wetter climate at sometime in the Pleistocene is widespread throughout the now desert areas of Asia, Arabia, China, and Australia. Pleistocene Lake Dieri of Australia sup- posedly covered at least 40,000 sq. miles and was surrounded by a dense rain forest!

Unfortunately exact climatic conditions over both the ice and periglacial areas are unknown, yet study of Pleistocene flora (and fauna) and snow line positions, combined with a consideration of pluvial lake hydrology and the known effects of precipitation and temperature on the glaciers, allows construction of several possible models, Fig.92 representing such a climatic curve.

As previously stated, debate rages over whether the ice age was caused by increased precipitation or decreased temperatures, Schwarzbach (1961b) reporting the consensus that decreased temperatures were responsible. Regardless of the temperatures at the start of glaciation it is agreed that world-wide temperatures were reduced as the glaciers expanded, somewhere in the neighbourhood of 8–12 °C (Bowen, 1966). At least a 7 °C drop would have occurred simply by the increased

TABLE XIV

INDICATED LOWERING OF PLEISTOCENE TEMPERATURES

Author	°C	
	summer	annual
ANDERSON (1961)	10.0	—
ANTEVS (1935)	—	3.0
ANTEVS (1952)	—	2.5–3.0
ANTEVS (1954)	3.0	—
BOWEN (1966)	—	8.0–12.0
BROECKER and ORR (1958)	—	5.0
BUTZER (1964)	7.0–9.0	—
DAVIS (1946)	7.0–8.0	—
DILLON (1956)	—	10.0
EMILIANI (1955a)	—	5.0–6.0
FLOHN (1953)	—	4.0
GAGEL (1923)	—	10.0
HARRIS and FINDLEY (1963)	6.0	—
HOSHIAI and KOBAYASHI (1957)	4.5–6.5	—
KAISER (1960)	—	15.0–16.0
KLUTE (1928)	4.0	2.0
KLUTE (1930)	—	4.0–5.0
LEOPOLD (1951)	9.0	6.5
LOUIS (1926)	—	5.5
MIKI (1956)	—	7.5
MORRISON (1965a)	—	4.0–8.0
PENCK (1928)	—	4.0
PENCK (1932)	—	5.0–6.0
PENCK (1938)	—	6.0
POTZGER and THARP (1947)	8.0	—
RANGE (1923)	—	10.0
REEVES (1965a, c, 1966b)	10.0	5.0
SCHAFER (1949	—	8.0
SCHNELL (1961)	—	8.0
SCHUMM (1965)	—	5.0
SHOTTON (1960)	—	13.5
SOERGEL (1937)	—	11.0
STEARNS (1942)	9.0	4.5
WENDORF (1961)	8.5–11.0	—
WERTH (1925)	—	10.0

albedo (DONN and EWING, 1966) and, to this, must be added the decrease caused by cloud cover and the ice mass (SOERGEL, 1937; EWING and DONN, 1958; LAMB, 1964; DONN and EWING, 1966). Table XIV lists indicated Pleistocene temperature reductions for various parts of the world as determined by several different investigators. The lowering of annual Pleistocene temperature ranges from 2 to 16 °C, and the lowering of the Pleistocene summer temperature ranges from 3 to 11 °C, the summer mean being about 7 °C and the winter mean about 10 °C. There is, therefore, a rather

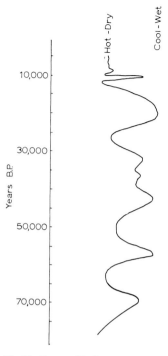

Fig.92. Curve of inferred climatic fluctuations in the eastern midwest of the United States. (Modified after MORRISON and FRYE, 1965.)

TABLE XV

MEAN ANNUAL TEMPERATURE RANGE FOR THE TERTIARY OF NORTHWEST EUROPE, WESTERN UNITED STATES, PACIFIC COAST OF NORTH AMERICA

(After DURHAM, 1950; WOLDSTEDT, 1954; DORF, 1955; SCHWARZBACH, 1961a, 1963; and BUTZER, 1964)

Epoch	Temperature range (°C)		
	Western U.S.	Pacific Coast, North America	Northwestern Europe
Recent	—	10	—
Pliocene	5–8	12	10–14
Miocene	9–14	11–18	16–19
Oligocene	14–18	18.5–20	18–20
Eocene	18–25	18.5–25	20–22
Paleocene	14.5	—	—

startling unanimity of opinion regarding the amount of Pleistocene temperature reduction even though some early Pleistocene investigators (WHITNEY, 1882; PILGRIM, 1904; SIMPSON, 1934) suggested that the glacial periods were warmer than the interglacials. Today (Table XV) there is ample evidence of deterioration of the mean annual temperature throughout the Cenozoic, thus most students of the Pleistocene suspect a world-wide falling of temperatures, but confined mainly to the summer months rather than a uniformly distributed temperature reduction throughout the year (CHARLESWORTH, 1957).

It is apparent that there is a voluminous amount of literature concerning the change *to* and *the* pluvial climates but a seemingly paucity of study of the interpluvial periods. Although a great deal of work has concerned the interpluvial periods (see CHARLESWORTH, 1957), students of the Pleistocene tend to consider the interpluvials as periods of "normal" climatic conditions. Actually much of the Yarmouthian and Sangamonian intervals in North America apparently were colder than today (F. C. BAKER, 1920; HAY, 1923; LEVERETT, 1929; COLEMAN, 1941), but evidence of soil profiles, plants, faunas, and $^{18}O/^{16}O$ isotope ratios from the European area indicates the Eem (about 75,000–65,000 years B.P.) interglacial was warmer than the present (BUTZER, 1964). The last interglacial period in Czechoslovakia was apparently $2°–3°C$ warmer than the present (KUKLA et al., 1961). QUINN (1958, 1961, 1965), on the basis of soil profiles, absence of Pleistocene cave faunas, orientation of drainage basins, ventifacts, and prairie mounds, thinks desert conditions causing pedimentation occurred in the Ozark Mountain region of Missouri–Arkansas during the Pleistocene interglacial periods.

Locations of the pluvial lakes, other than being controlled by the displaced belt of westerlies, were also dependent on availability of basins, thus most of the pluvial lakes in the Great American Desert formed in pre-existing intermontane basins. However, in West Texas most of the large pluvial basins were formed by a combination of erosion by pluvial streams and deflation by interpluvial winds (REEVES, 1965d, 1966a). Such stream-associated pluvial basins are also known from Australia (DAVID, 1950) and Africa (ROGERS, 1922; JAEGER, 1939; WELLINGTON, 1943, 1945), but caution must be exercised in that a basin-related channel may reflect simply overflow rather than genesis (Fig.93).

The recognition of ancient lake basins therefore is not difficult. Any closed to near-closed valley in present arid to semi-arid areas should be immediately suspect, proof dependent mainly on the presence of lacustrine precipitates, lacustrine and eolian clastics, and abandoned shorelines.

Playas and paleolake basins are almost universally flanked on one side by dune areas, the dune composition reflecting adjacent playa mineralogy. Thus most dunes are of fine-grained quartz, sand, clay, silt, gypsum, or fine carbonate grains. The larger of the dunes are either of transverse or sand sheet type, the transverse dunes often rising over 100 ft. above the playas (Fig.33). One of the best examples perhaps of a leeward sand sheet originating due to a nearby paleolake basin is the Medaños area of northwest Chihuahua, Mexico. The Medaños, rising 300 ft. where they

Fig.93. The Goyder Channel joining Lake Eyre North to Lake Eyre South, South Australia. The channel is due to overflow and has no genetic relation to the lake basin. No overflow from one lake to another is known to have occurred during historic time. Lake Eyre is in the background. (Photo by courtesy of C. Warren Bonython.)

accumulate against the Sierra del Presidio, cover about 1,000 sq. miles, calling particular attention to the Palomas basin on their windward side.

Some abandoned shorelines, like those from Lake Bonneville or Lake Buchanan, Australia (Fig.94), are particularly striking because of their parallelism and continuity, but development of a strong shoreline depends not only on length of time of existence of the lake, combined with wind direction and lithology, but on size of the lake. Naturally a large lake like Bonneville (20,000 sq. miles) tended to develop much better shorelines than Guthrie Lake, Texas (30 sq. miles) or T-Bar Lake, Texas, with an area of only 9 sq. miles (Fig.95), yet age is a most important factor in shoreline recognition. The easily recognizable, wave-cut shorelines of paleolake basins throughout the world are mainly of Wisconsin age, pre-Wisconsin shorelines being recognized principally by lacustrine sediments, beach gravels, or the abutment of suspected lacustrine debris against flanking highland areas, as occurs in the Hueco Basin, Texas and New Mexico.

If a lake, after being at high-level stand for some time, suddenly loses water rapidly, no multiple shorelines of regression would be produced, and likewise, if a basin rapidly accumulates water no transgressive shorelines are formed. This then

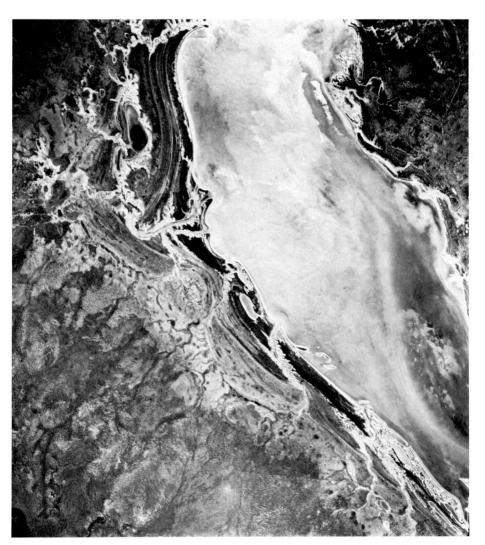

Fig.94. Lake Buchanan, Australia, approximate position being 22°S 146°W. Notice abandoned shorelines, bars, and spits along the west side. R. W. Galloway (personal communication, 1967) recognizes two abandoned beach levels, one at 10–20 ft. and a second at 40 ft. above the present playa, the higher beach probably of pre-Wisconsin age. (Photo by courtesy of the Director, Division of National Mapping, Department of National Development, Canberra, A.C.T., Australia.)

Fig.95. The abandoned shorelines on the west side of T-Bar Lake, Lynn County, Texas. The present playa level is immediately to the right. (Photo by the author.)

Fig.96. Fault scarp along east flank of San Andres Mountains, New Mexico, west of Lake Lucero, White Sands Missile Range. This fault (verified by well control) escarpment has apparently been notched (arrow) by a post-fault lake (Palomas?) that once flooded the Tularosa Basin. (Photo by the author.)

may make recognition of isolated, high-level shorelines difficult, especially if they have been altered by erosion, displaced by tectonic movements, or buried by erosional debris. This is currently the case for many of the Wisconsin-aged shorelines of pluvial lakes Palomas, Mexico and the United States, Bonneville, Utah, and Lahontan, Nevada (HAWLEY and WILSON, 1965) and undoubtedly the principal reason why pre-Wisconsin shorelines are so difficult to find.

Recent fault scarps can easily be confused with recent, abandoned lacustrine shorelines, especially when within or near an abandoned lake basin. However, the fact that an escarpment is due basically to faulting certainly does not prevent lake water from backing against it, in fact, field evidence from several areas in the southwestern United States indicates that such a relation has been rather common (Fig.96). Unfortunately where fault escarpments give way to only wave-cut shorelines is generally not determinable.

An excellent example of a fault scarp – abandoned shoreline relation exists east of Columbus, New Mexico, where pluvial Lake Palomas once backed against a fault, the displacement verified by well control, the lake level by lacustrine strata. Thirty miles to the south, in Chihuahua, Mexico, the same escarpment persists (Fig. 97), but whether the escarpment here represents a fault or only a young wave-cut feature is unknown.

Displacement of shorelines caused by post-lacustrine tectonic movements, combined with destruction by erosion or faulting can effectively mask an ancient lake level, probably because most investigators, when looking for abandoned shore-

Fig.97. Aerial photograph of the Bonneville–Lahontan aged La Mota beach, northeastern flank of Lake Palomas, Chihuahua, Mexico. Sporadic exposures of lacustrine clays, sands, and carbonates as well as wave-cut terraces, fix the old lake level. (Photo by the author.)

lines, expect to find perfectly horizontal features. Warped shorelines are known from many of the pluvial lake basins in the Great American Desert, the best documented being those associated with Lake Bonneville. GILBERT (1890) found the Great Salt Lake basin had, in spots, uplifted as much as 180 ft. since Bonneville time, recent study (CRITTENDEN, 1963) indicating at least 210 ft. Considerable uplift of abandoned shorelines of Lake Palomas, Mexico, also has occurred, thus the argument that certain features are not ancient lacustrine shorelines because they slope from one area to another is, in itself, invalid.

One of the most helpful tools in locating ancient lake basins is an aerial photograph. Abandoned shorelines (Fig.94, 96, 97), bars and spits (Fig.80–83), playas and playa structures (Fig.68–77) show very well on large-scale photos and regional outlines of large ancient lakes are well exhibited on small-scale aerial photographs (Frontispiece), thus a good command of aerial photographic interpretation is fundamental for good paleolimnological studies. Certainly, in the future as increased aerial photographic coverage of our celestial neighbors becomes available, the search for, and recognition and study of, ancient lakes, their features and basins, will be of great importance to our space effort in interpretation of past or present celestial environments and in selection of landing sites.

Chapter 10

PALEOCLIMATIC METHODS

The determination of past climatic parameters by the use of paleohydrologic conditions is an important phase of paleoclimatology. The present climate of any local area, on any continent, and around any lake basin, depends on the same factors which controlled Pleistocene climate. The study of present meteorological conditions is then a perfect application of the present being the "key to the past."

The present climate for *any* area of the earth is controlled by innumerable and diverse variables, the same variables that undoubtedly controlled the paleoclimate of any particular area during any period of earth history. The variables of major interest are the distribution of continents, oceans, and precipitations, and the directions of the prevailing wind patterns and ocean currents. The earth's temperatures and climates are basically controlled by the amount of solar radiation and the inclination of the earth to the sun.

The inclination of earth's axis ranges, over a 41,000 year period, from 21 °8′ to 24 °4′ (BROUWER and VAN WOERKOM, 1950), presently being about 23 °30′ Thus, the amount of solar radiation (insolation) received depends first of all on the axial tilt, becoming less and less at one pole but more and more at the opposite pole (at any one time) as the angle of tilt increases. Since the earth is a near sphere it is axiomatic that, regardless of tilt of the axis in the past, climatic zones existed. Open and closed lake basins must then have also existed in various widespread geographic areas.

As any globe shows, there is a tremendous difference in the distribution of the continents and ocean basins between the hemispheres. In the Southern Hemisphere the area between about 35 ° to 65 °S latitude has the greatest concentration of water, some 98 %, while in the Northern Hemisphere the area between 45 ° and 70 °N latitude has the greatest land area. Because the continental areas tend to cause great differences in climatic extremes, while oceans tend to modify such extremes, the warmest summer and coldest winter areas are presently over the continental masses of the Northern Hemisphere.

The air currents of the earth, and consequently the ocean currents, are controlled mainly by the rotation of the earth and the contrasting temperature differences between the polar and equatorial areas. Theoretically the hot ascending air of the equatorial regions creates a vacuum or low pressure zone into which the colder air from the polar regions rushes; however, because of the vast continental areas and rotation of the earth the polar air masses are deflected into local pressure centers, the overall movement near the equator being westward.

Principal wind movements of the earth, such as the northeast trades of the

Northern Hemisphere and the southeast trades of the Southern Hemisphere, create ocean currents; thus the ocean currents between about 24 °N and 24 °S latitude flow westward. Of course oceanic water movements are also caused by changes in water density produced by temperature differences between polar and equatorial water. Whether ocean currents flowing next to a continent are cold or warm then exerts considerable influence on local climate.

The distribution of precipitation, past and present, has been and is basically controlled by all of the preceding factors. For instance, precipitation is generally heaviest over or on continental fringes near the ocean basins. In latitudes where wind patterns rise there is generally precipitation, unless passing over the land heats the air. Descending air patterns are characteristic of deserts, for the air, heating as it descends, effectively soaks up excess moisture.

Many methods exist which help in determining paleoclimatic conditions. The most popular probably concern the study of sand dunes, coal measures, and spores and pollen although considerable attention is also devoted to the fossil plants, associated macro- and micro-fossils, paleohydrologic conditions, and to chemistry of lacustrine sediments. The pluvial–interpluvial relationships of midges (STAHL, 1959), molluscs (TAYLOR, 1965), gastropods (FRYE and LEONARD, 1957a, b), diatoms (ROUND, 1961; HOHN and HELLERMAN, 1961), the invertebrates, and a wide selection of vertebrates, have also been studied.

HYDROLOGIC STUDIES

The determination of paleoclimatic conditions by hydroclimatic study is based on quantitative methods and therefore gives purely quantitative results, unfortunately seldom having room for error or climatic parameters which knowingly vary from year to year.

Precipitation and runoff

Of the many climatic parameters those most intimately associated with lake levels are: (*1*) the distribution, type, and amount of precipitation, (*2*) the amount of runoff into and out of the basin, and (*3*) the maximum, minimum, and general temperature march which controls, to some extent, the evaporation rate; of the three, evaporation is most constant. If the lake basin is closed a delicate balance exists between lake area, runoff, and evaporation, disregarding seepage or transpiration by aquatic vegetation; however, before examining these relations, let us first individually and critically examine the mentioned hydroclimatic parameters.

Precipitation is atmosphere moisture falling on the surface of the earth in the form of rain, hail, sleet, snow, or ice, the greater amount in most areas occurring as rainfall. Neglecting precipitation on a lake's surface, the amount of inflow depends on runoff from the surrounding basin, the runoff always being less than the precipi-

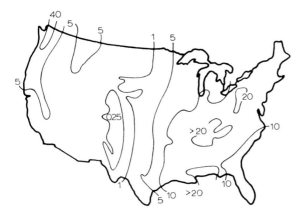

Fig.98. Highly generalized map of runoff in the United States. Notice the general decrease in runoff from east to west, the paucity in the Great American desert area, and the increase next to the West Coast. However, there are numerous small mountain areas in the western interior where runoff ranges from 5 to 20 inches. (Modified after LANGBEIN, 1949.)

tation. Runoff arises from the amount of precipitation remaining after evaporation and infiltration, from snow and glacial melt water, and from escape of ground water. In many areas, such as the Llano Estacado of West Texas, runoff approaches zero, other considerations not withstanding. Runoff tends to decrease in areas of permeable surface debris or in highly vegetated areas. If precipitation remains steady runoff will decrease with rising temperatures, but likewise will increase with falling temperatures and increasing altitude, at least until the freezing temperature is reached. Estimation of paleorunoff from present figures may then become a source of considerable error if unknown or unsuspected topographic, vegetative, or lithologic changes have occurred in the drainage basin, let alone changes that may have taken place in the other climatic parameters.

Fig.98 is a map of average annual runoff for the United States. Notice how runoff increases with elevation, even in the midst of the western desert areas. Many of the long, narrow mountain ranges of eastern Nevada have a runoff of over 30 inches in places, 20 inches being quite common (BAILEY, 1941).

Because of the relative short period of geologic time involved, changes in lithology and topography need not be seriously considered when working with Pleistocene lake basins, thus the runoff fluctuations can be considered to result mainly from climatological factors. Yet, it should be realized that changes of vegetation attendant with the climatic changes probably had some slight effect.

Because temperature has the most dramatic effect on runoff, by control of the evaporation rate, a near generalized relation exists between annual precipitation, mean annual temperature, and annual runoff (Fig.99). LANGBEIN (1949), in developing his graph (Fig.99), used a *weighted mean temperature* derived by division of the products of monthly temperature and precipitation by annual precipitation. This takes into account the effect of most precipitation falling in the warm part of the year

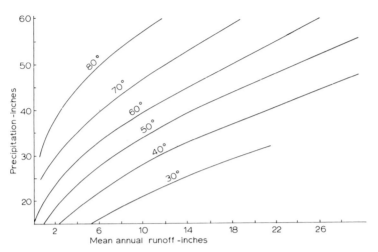

Fig.99. The more or less linear relation that ideally exists between annual runoff, annual temperature, and annual precipitation. The central parameters represent mean annual temperature. (Modified after LANGBEIN 1949, 1961.)

(weighed temperature greater than mean temperature) or in the cooler months (weighed temperature smaller than mean temperature). The well-known *rain factor* is not nearly as effective as the weighted mean temperature simply because it correlates only the rainfall–temperature relation whereas personal distribution of precipitation must also be observed.

Caution must be exercised in applying Fig.99. The relations developed are only generalizations and are subject to great change by topography or lithology. For instance, Fig.99 shows that the Lubbock, Texas, area and most of the High Plains should experience a runoff about four times the 0.25 inch/year that actually exists, the reduction taking place because of little relief, permeable surface debris underlaid by an impermeable layer, poor drainage development, and a high evaporation rate (LANGBEIN, 1949; REEVES, 1965c, 1966d).

Of some importance to runoff is the distribution of precipitation. If precipitation occurs mainly during the warm months, which it supposedly did during pluvial times (MANLEY, 1955; DILLON, 1956), runoff will be less than if precipitation occurs mainly during the colder months, unity naturally occuring with equal monthly rainfalls and temperatures (SNYDER and LANGBEIN, 1962). The variation of this, the *seasonal factor*, and its effects are shown by Fig.100, a graph of the ratio of runoff to potential evaporation against the ratio of annual precipitation over potential evaporation. The seasonal factor (*SF*) for any area is computed by adding the products of monthly precipitation (P_j, P_f, P_m . . . P_d) by mean monthly evaporation (E_j, E_f, E_m . . . E_d) and dividing into mean annual precipitation (P) times mean monthly evaporation (E_{mm}):

$$SF = \frac{E_{mm}P_{ma}}{(E_jP_j) + (E_fP_f) + \ldots (E_dP_d)}$$

The runoff of a lake basin is responsible for the amount of sediment removed from the basin and carried into the lake proper, but sediment yield *is not* a linear function of precipitation. Rather, as precipitation increases sediment yield increases, but the increased water regimen soon causes a reversal in sediment yield as vegetation is established to effectively decrease runoff.

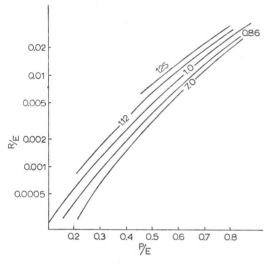

Fig.100. Graph of the ratio of annual runoff to potential evaporation (R/E) against the ratio of annual precipitation to potential evaporation (P/E) which gives the season precipitation factor. The five parameters are various seasonal factors. (Modified after SNYDER and LANGBEIN, 1962.)

Evaporation

The evaporation rate is of particular interest to paleolimnologists and paleo-climatologists especially when dealing with closed lake basins. The evaporation rate, the change from a liquid or solid to a gas, depends on many variables as humidity, water purity, vapor pressure, topography, wind speed, barometric pressure, and extent of the water surface. Theoretically, the variable of greatest importance to the evaporation of water from a lake surface would be water temperature (Fig.101), for temperature increases the vapor pressure, thus the colder the water the lower the evaporation. However, it has been determined that (lake) evaporation depends not necessarily on temperature of either the air or the water, but on relative differences between the two (ROHWER, 1931).

Humidity or the amount of atmospheric water vapor, exerts a very definite control over lake evaporation. Obviously, if the atmosphere is saturated with water vapor (100% humidity), no evaporation (i.e., escape of water molecules from the lake surface) will occur. Wind, unlike humidity, is more or less directly related to evaporation, the evaporation increasing with the wind velocity. Low atmospheric

Fig.101. Mean monthly surface water temperature (°F) for July–August in the western United States. (Modified after Miller, et al., 1963.)

(barometric) pressure also enhances evaporation. Unfortunately, what quantitative value most of these factors had on an ancient lake is undeterminable, therefore they are of little use to the paleolimnologist.

Certainly annual temperature and annual precipitation exert the major influence on the evaporation rate in any area, the greater the precipitation the lower the evaporation because of increased relative humidity and cloudiness. The ideal relations between evaporation, temperature, and precipitation are shown in Fig.102, the relations with net evaporation from a closed lake in Fig.103.

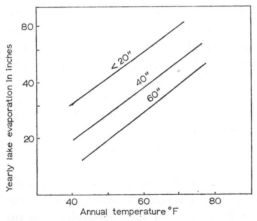

Fig.102. The ideal linear relation that exists between gross annual lake evaporation, annual temperature, and annual precipitation. The three central parameters represent mean annual precipitation. (Modified after LANGBEIN, 1961.)

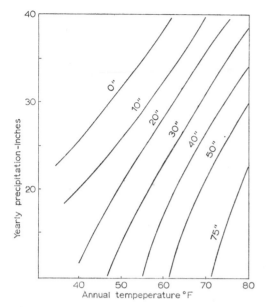

Fig.103. The relation between annual temperature, annual precipitation, and the net evaporation from a closed lake. The central parameters represent the net evaporation in inches. (Modified after LANGBEIN, 1961.)

Evaporation studies were initiated by the U.S. Department of Agriculture in 1905, but concerned mainly losses of water from soils. Reports on evaporation rates from different types and sizes of evaporation pans appeared in the early 1930's (ROHWER, 1931, 1934), and in 1952 and 1958 detailed water-loss studies from Lake Hefner, Oklahoma, and Lake Meade, Nevada, were released by the U.S. Geological Survey. In 1959 KOHLER et al. published *Evaporation Maps for the United States*, perhaps the most comprehensive and concise data available at the time. Fig.104, taken from Kohler et al. (1959) study, shows generalized lake evaporation for the western United States.

The four principal methods of determining evaporation from a lake area are: (*1*) by examination of the energy relations between the lake and surrounding environment; (*2*) by examination of the water budget of the lake; (*3*) by examination of boundary-layer phenomena at the lake's surface, and (*4*) by relation to pan evaporation studies. Measurement of energy relations and study of boundary-layer phenomena necessitates complex instrumentation generally not available to most paleolimnologists, and water budget studies suffer from inaccuracies inherent in computation of runoff into and precipitation on the lake plus seepage from the lake. Also, variables in evaporation studies by boundary-layer, water or energy budget studies are measured in association with the lake water, thus of the four methods only pan evaporation studies offer reasonable application for paleolimnological work. However, because evaporation estimates for old lake basins may be assumed by correlation with present environments, let us first briefly discuss the first three methods. For those interested in derivation of formulas presented or methods of measurement

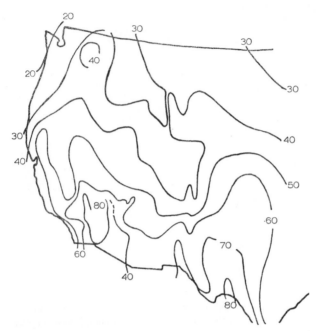

Fig.104. Generalized map of the average annual lake evaporation, in inches, for the western United States. (Modified after KOHLER et al., 1959.)

of the variables I suggest reference to either E. R. ANDERSON (1954), HARBECK et al. (1958), or SELLERS (1965).

Water budget

The computation of evaporation by examining the water budget of a lake is perhaps the least involved of the methods to be discussed and may yield very inaccurate results because of difficulties in measuring the variables involved. The water budget of a lake can be represented by the equation:

$$LE = LI - LO - LC + LP$$

where LE = lake evaporation; LI = lake inflow; LO = lake outflow; LC = lake change due to thermal expansion and contraction, and LP = precipitation on the lake. If runoff or precipitation in an area is very high or quite variable from season to season, large errors may exist in LI but if runoff is low the accuracy of LI is increased. Likewise, if the lake basin is open or leaky, complications arise in gauging LO; however, if the basin is closed and tightly sealed, LO may be disregarded. LC is very difficult to determine even for existing lakes, depending on the thermal expansion coefficient for water and the temperature change of the water, thus in deep lakes depth to the thermocline must be known as well as the change in water temperature experienced by the epilimnion—data naturally unavailable for any paleolake.

Energy budget

The energy budget for a lake is expressed by the equation:

$$Q_\theta = Q_s - Q_r + Q_a - Q_{ar} - Q_{bs} + Q_v - Q_e - Q_h - Q_w$$

where Q_s = solar radiation on the lake surface; Q_r = solar radiation reflected; Q_a = atmospheric long-wave radiation; Q_{ar} = atmospheric long-wave radiation reflected; Q_{bs} = long-wave radiation from the lake water; Q_e = evaporation energy; Q_h = energy from the lake; Q_v = energy advected into the lake; Q_w = energy advected by evaporated lake water; and Q_θ = energy increase in the lake (HARBECK et al., 1958). These relations lead to the evaporation equation:

$$E = \frac{Q_s - Q_r + Q_a - Q_{ar} - Q_{bs} - Q_\theta + Q_v}{\varrho e[L(1+R) + C(T_e - T_b)]}$$

where ϱe = the density of the evaporated water; L = the latent heat of vaporization; R = the Bowen ratio; C = the specific heat of water; T_e = the temperature of the eva-porated lake water; and T_b = the arbitary base temperature (E. R. ANDERSON, 1954).

If these variables can be judiciously studied and accurately measured, a reason-able evaporation rate is secured; however, since an energy-budget study can be used with paleolakes only by assumption of the majority of the variables, it is best applied only to present reservoirs.

Boundary-layer

Boundary-layer or mass transfer studies concern the evaporation of lake water mainly due to wind speed and vapor-pressure differences. Several equations exist (THORNWAITE and HOLZMAN, 1939; SVERDRUP, 1946; CALDER, 1949; HARBECK et al., 1958); however, the extensive U.S. Geological Survey studies at Lake Hefner, Oklahoma, and Lake Meade, Arizona, showed that equations applicable to one lake gave misleading results at the other lake. Which mass transfer equation to use when studying a present lake is then conjectural, and generally empirical equa-tions developed from observed evaporation work best. Unfortunately this cannot be done with paleolakes, yet since variables must be assumed the margin of error in these assumptions is undoubtedly as great as that between the different equations. For this reason, the SVERDRUP (1937) equation, which gave good results at Lake Hefner, Oklahoma, (E. R. ANDERSON, 1954) is provided for those who might want to play with application to a paleolake:

$$E = \frac{0.623 \, pk_0 u_* \, (e_0 - e_z)}{P\left[ln\left(\frac{z + z_0}{\delta + z_0}\right) + \frac{k_0 \delta_1 u_*}{D}\right]}$$

where p = density of the air; k_0 = the Von Karman constant; u_* = the friction velocity; e_0 = the vapor pressure of saturated air at the temperature of the water surface; e_z = the vapor pressure of the air at height z; P = the atmospheric pressure; z = distance along a vertical coordinate axis; z_0 = the roughness parameter; δ_1 = thickness of the laminar film; and D = the molecular vapor diffusity.

The SVERDRUP (1937) equation unfortunately gave inaccurate results when applied to study of Lake Meade, thus the development of the empirical equation:

$$E = 2.65 \cdot 10^{-3} \, U_8 \, (e_0 - e_8)$$

where U_8 = average wind speed at 2 m height; e_0 = vapor pressure of saturated air at temperature of the lake water surface; and e_8 = vapor pressure of air at the 2 m height (HARBECK et al., 1958). The empirical equation for use at Lake Hefner was:

$$E = 6.25 \cdot 10^{-4} \, U_8 \, (e_0 - e_8)$$

which utilized data from the 8 m height.

Pan evaporation

Tests, from all different types of evaporation pans, indicate that pan evaporation is always greater than that from a lake surface. the coefficients shown in Table XVI based on studies by YOUNG (1942, 1947a). The Young Screen Pan comes nearest to approaching unity, followed by the Plant Industry Pan.

TABLE XVI

AVERAGE COEFFICIENTS FOR VARIOUS EVAPORATION PANS

Pan type	Coefficient
Bureau of Plant Industry	0.94
Colorado	0.89
Weather Bureau Class A	0.77–0.70
Young Screen	0.98

The long standing rule has been to use a coefficient of 0.70 for the Weather Bureau Class A pan when estimating lake evaporation, a method which has yielded surprisingly accurate results during actual studies as long as the lake does not experience a change in energy storage. Fig.105 illustrates the evaporation from a Class A pan throughout the western United States, Fig.106 showing the regional coefficients. As the Lake Meade studies showed (HARBECK et al., 1958), the evaporation by coefficient should closely approximate the evaporation by the equation:

$$E_L = 0.70 \left(\frac{Qn\Delta + Ea\gamma}{\Delta + \gamma} \right)$$

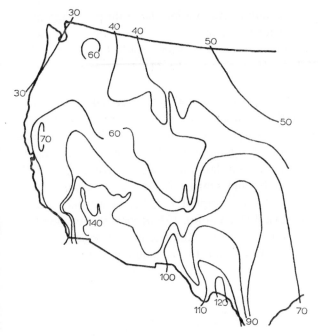

Fig.105. Generalized map of the average annual Class A pan evaporation, in inches, for the western United States. (Modified after KOHLER et al., 1959.)

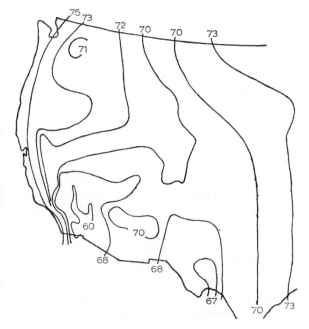

Fig.106. Generalized map of the average annual Class A pan coefficient, in per cent, for the western United States. (Modified after KOHLER et al., 1959.)

where Qn = net radiation in the same units as evaporation; Ea = the pan evaporation providing air temperature equals water temperature; Δ = the slope of saturation vapor pressure versus the temperature curve; and γ = an empirical constant.

Young's studies and the Lake Hefner and Lake Meade programs were, of course, based on fresh water which means that applicability to saline lakes is somewhat reduced. Thus BLANEY's (1957) evaporation study at Silver Lake, California, indicates a coefficient of 0.60 for the Weather Bureau Class A pan. Evaporation from a salt lake, irrespective of other conditions, depends on humidity, salinity, and type of salt in solution, the evaporation being more or less inversely proportional to the per cent increase of salinity; thus, as a saline lake evaporates the evaporation tends to decrease as the lake becomes smaller and saltier.[1] A rate of evaporation, then from Great Salt Lake would be expected to be about 75% less than from an equivalent fresh-water surface. Studies (LEE, 1927; YOUNG, 1947b) show that evaporation decreases, to a certain point, about 1% for every 0.01 rise in specific gravity. The idealized relation of fresh-water lake evaporation to precipitation and temperature is shown by Fig.102.

DEVELOPMENT OF FORMULAS

If a lake is closed, the annual hydroclimatic relation can be determined because precipitation (*LP*) on the lake plus runoff from the surrounding basin (*BR*) must equal lake evaporation (*LE*), or:

$$LP + BR = LE$$

If the lake is open, then runoff of the influent (*IR*) and runoff of the effluent (*ER*) must be added so that the equation becomes:

$$LP + BR + IR = LE + ER$$

The use of these equations with present lakes is not difficult or even necessary, unless seepage is suspected, but application to ancient lake basins is extremely profitable. These equations then are basic in estimating what climatic conditions prevailed when ancient lakes existed, but are generally used in expanded forms depending on local conditions.

Several formulas are used to equate ancient lake areas to precipitation, runoff, evaporation, and basin areas (ANTEVS, 1935; LEOPOLD, 1951; BROECKER and ORR, 1958; LANGBEIN, 1961; BRADLEY, 1963), the clearest explanation perhaps following LANGBEIN's (1961) work. The first consideration of the proposal shown by the previous equations is that lake area (*LA*) results from precipitation on the lake (*LP*) plus basin

---

[1] See PENMAN (1955) and BONYTHON (1955) for evaporation from a saline solution.

runoff (BR) plus influent runoff (IR) minus the sum of evaporation from the lake (LE) plus effluent runoff, or:

$$LA = LP + BR + IR - (LE + ER)$$

For closed lakes the equation becomes:

$$LA = LP + BR - LE$$

Since the ratio of any lake area (LA) to its basin area (BA) approaches unity as the lake increases in size, amount of runoff (R) will depend on the ratio LA/BA, runoff decreasing as lake area increases. Thus, a closed lake existing under equilibrium conditions is represented by the equation:

$$\frac{LA}{BA} = \frac{R}{LP - LE}$$

However, a difference generally exists in amount of evaporation and precipitation between the lake surface and the surrounding basin area, especially when the basin exhibits considerable relief. This occurs because evaporation decreases about 6% for each 1,000 ft. increase in altitude while precipitation increases. Evaporation over the basin (BE) then is equal to lake evaporation (LE) minus an evaporation amount (e) due to precipitation on the lake, or $LE = BE + e$, while average precipitation over the basin (BP) equals lake precipitation (LP) plus the precipitation amount (p), or $LP = BP - p$ (SNYDER and LANGBEIN, 1962). This is represented by the following equation where LA/BA equals LA':

$$LA' = \frac{R}{(BE + e + p - BP)}$$

$$LA' = \frac{R/BE}{1 + \dfrac{e}{BE} - \dfrac{BP}{BE} + \dfrac{p}{BE}}$$

$$LA' = \frac{R/BE}{1 - \dfrac{BP}{BE} + \dfrac{e+p}{BE}}$$

If the surrounding basin is relatively devoid of relief, so that there is little imbalance of evaporation and precipitation between the lake surface and the surrounding basin the term $e + p/BE$ may be excluded, giving:

$$LA' = \frac{R/BE}{1 - \dfrac{BP}{BE}}$$

BROECKER and ORR (1958) have also developed an equation representing a situation when precipitation and runoff into a lake equals evaporation from the lake, but where only local basin runoff is considered:

$$A_{\text{lake}} = \frac{fr}{le/lr + fr - 1} A_{\text{basin}}$$

where fr equals runoff into the lake from the basin only, le equals average evaporation, and lr equals average precipitation. The equation is developed in the following manner (W. S. Broecker, personal communication, 1966):

$$(A_{\text{lake}}) (lr) + (A_{\text{basin}} - A_{\text{lake}}) \, lrfr = A_{\text{lake}} \, le$$

$$(A_{\text{lake}}) (lr) + A_{\text{basin}} \, lrfr - A_{\text{lake}} \, lrfr = A_{\text{lake}} \, le$$
$$A_{\text{lake}} (lr - lrfr - le) = - A_{\text{basin}} \, lrfr$$

$$A_{\text{lake}} = \frac{lrfr}{le + lrfr - lr} A_{\text{basin}}$$

$$A_{\text{lake}} = \frac{fr}{le/fr + fr - 1} A_{\text{basin}}$$

The determination of the paleohydroclimatic relations which existed when present dry abandoned lake basins contained water is, of course, the essence of paleolimnology. Inherent in any equation expressing the water budget of a lake are variables such as runoff, precipitation, and evaporation; the area of the lake and basin are generally rather accurately determined. The primary mode of attack then is to determine, at least within some narrow limits, parameters for two of the variables and solve for the third.

An area exhibiting abandoned lake basins probably has less rainfall and runoff, but more potential evaporation, than when the lake contained water, thus present hydroclimatic relations can generally be considered as minimums for precipitation and runoff and a maximum for evaporation. Of the three variables, runoff would, at first, seem to be the most limited, because of control due to lithology, topography, and vegetation. Certainly lithologic and topographic changes are much slower than changes in the climatic environment, but this only means that the ratio $(e + p)/BE$ was probably little different during the actual lake period than it is today, a slight expected change occurring due to present scarcity of vegetation. Runoff may have been much greater, even in areas with an $(e + p)/BE$ ratio of zero, particularly if large streams once existed.

Many mountainous areas, especially in the western United States, are adjacent to ancient pluvial lake basins. Fortunately the higher peaks of these mountains, at least as far south as 35° 20′ N lat. (in the state of New Mexico), were glaciated during the pluvial periods, the lower elevation of the cirques of any one age representing the local *snow line* of that particular time. The *snow line*, defined by FLINT (1947) as the line separating the higher areas of perennial snow on a mountain from the lower summer snow-free areas, is actually a very irregular zone, the lower limit of which is termed the *orographic snow line*. Sun radiation and prevailing winds cause the snow line to vary from one part of a mountain to another, thus the mean value of the different values can be taken as the *climatic snow line*. It is the orographic snow line which more or less corresponds to the lower limits of the cirques.

The position of the present or any ancient snow line must always be suspect because it is so easily altered by so many variables. Primarily the snow line position depends on temperature and precipitation, the snow line rising with increasing temperature or less precipitation. There is a general rise of the snow line both north and south of the equator into the "Horse" Latitudes, from which it steadily falls toward both poles. However, because the great land areas of the Northern Hemisphere drastically reduce precipitation, the snow line comes within 9° of the pole in the Greenland area. In the Southern Hemisphere, with its vast ocean areas, the snow line reaches sea level as much as 37° from the pole. Snow line temperatures and studies are fully discussed by KÖPPEN (1920), AHLMANN (1924), MORAWETZ, (1955), TROLL (1956), and BUTZER (1964).

The importance of snow line positions in paleolimnological studies hinges on the correlation of an abandoned lake level with a particular snow line. If an abandoned lake level can be correlated with a particular abandoned snow line, the mid-summer and mean annual temperatures that existed when the lake was at its ancient level can be roughly computed by using the *lapse rate*.

The normal *lapse rate*, defined as the average rate of decrease of temperature with increasing altitude, is supposedly about 3.5°F/1,000 ft., regardless of where or when measured (KOEPPE and DE LONG, 1958). However, many studies indicate that the lapse rate varies somewhat seasonally and geographically. F. S. BAKER (1944), from studies throughout the mountainous regions of the western United States, found the average January lapse rate to be about 3.0°F/1,000 ft., but 3.5°F/1,000 ft. during the month of July. Not only is the lapse rate variable, but evidence (FLOHN, 1952) shows an actual inversion up to about 5,000 ft. may occur whereby surface temperatures much lower than expected by lapse extrapolation may actually exist (METEOROLOGICAL DIVISION, 1944). Whether such inversions existed during Pleistocene glacial periods is unknown but highly probable from evidence at hand (MORTENSEN, 1952; WRIGHT, 1961).

Because snow line position is controlled mainly by summer temperatures (ANTEVS, 1928; KLUTE, 1928; FLINT, 1947; LEOPOLD, 1951), a difference between the snow line and a nearby area, on or near the same latitude, may be equated to the temperature difference which existed in the area at the time of snow existence, providing snow line temperature and lapse rate are arbitrarily considered to have been their present approximate average figures. Naturally this computation then gives the temperature of positions below the snow line. However, it should be realized that the local temperatures and hence the lapse rate, could have been influenced by topography, cloud cover, ratio of snow to overall precipitation, or even radiation changes. Of course, this rate of increase only takes place up to certain elevations, well above the earth's topography, after which air temperature remains about steady. Changes in pressure of rising or falling air produces temperature changes, the rate of change termed the *adiabatic lapse rate*; however, these are too impermanent to be considered for paleoclimatological determinations.

Although evidence from Europe indicates lower temperatures for both Pleistocene summers and winters, considerable evidence suggests that winter temperatures south of the Pleistocene glacial fronts were little different from today's (HARMER, 1901; LEOPOLD, 1951; ODUM, 1952). Maximum chilling apparently occurred during the summer months (CHARLESWORTH, 1957). Difference then in the elevations of the ancient lake level and the local snow line, multiplied by the lapse rate, gives an approximation of the mean monthly mid-summer temperature when the lake-ice existed, providing no difference in latitude exists between cirque and lake.[1] When the mid-summer and winter (December and January) temperatures are known, a temperature march can be constructed, the interim mean monthly temperatures reduced proportionally (LEOPOLD, 1951).

A hysteresis loop, resulting from connection of the 12 positions which designate the amount of mean monthly evaporation by the mean monthly temperature, allows construction of a pluvial hysteresis loop, the pluvial temperatures as derived from the constructed temperature march (Fig.107). Addition of the monthly figures then gives

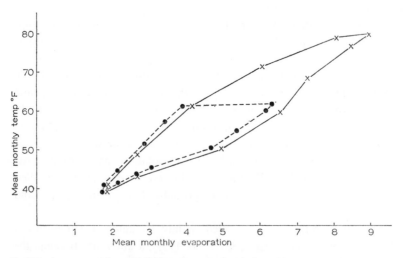

Fig.107. A present (x's–solid line) and a calculated Cary (dots–dashed line) hysteresis loop for the southern High Plains, Lubbock, Texas, area, produced from evaporation of a Bureau of Plant Industry Pan. There is no correction for the present loop but the Cary loop, which is determined by temperatures calculated in Fig.109, is corrected by a BPI coefficient of 0.94. (Modified after REEVES, 1965c.)

---

[1] Temperature adjustments for latitude differences can also be made if necessary.

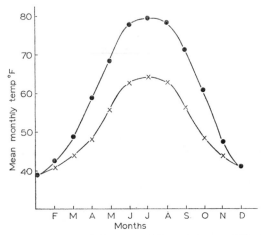

Fig.108. Graph of mean monthly temperature (°F) plotted against each month, for the southern High Plains, Lubbock, Texas, area. The dots represent the present temperature march, the *x*'s the computed Cary temperature march based on nearby cirque levels and the present lapse rate. (Modified after REEVES, 1965c.)

the pluvial evaporation rate. The present and Late Pleistocene (Cary) calculated temperature march for the southern High Plains, Texas, based on Pleistocene cirques on Cerro Blanco, New Mexico, and the pluvial lakes of West Texas, is shown in Fig.108, the addition of the monthly evaporation figures then giving the Cary evaporation rate for the West Texas area.

Of prime importance is the accuracy of such a derived evaporation rate. Obviously sources of possible error are in assuming that the local snow line accurately marks the position of the pluvial 32 °F isotherm[1], or in assuming that a certain cirque and lake level were penecontemporaneous. Thorough field geology should insure proper correlation of cirque and lake levels and there is no reason to suspect that pluvial lapse rates were significantly different from today's, but such is not the case with pluvial snow lines. A local pluvial snow line may have been much higher or much lower than the regional snow line; due perhaps to topography, vegetation, lithology, wind, or precipitation, an abundance of snow particularly tending to produce an abnormal depression. Local depressions of ancient snow lines can often be revealed by examination of snow lines in adjacent area.

Fig.102 and 103 show the interrelation between precipitation, temperature, and evaporation from a lake surface. Using the evaporation rate derived from construction of the hysteresis loop then gives an infinite series of precipitation–temperature combinations for an area, but unfortunately does not pinpoint the exact combination that existed during the pluvial time being investigated. For instance, assuming an evaporation of 20 inches (Fig.102) gives a precipitation range from about 25 to 60 inches and an annual temperature range from 30 to 50 °F, an

[1] Snow line temperature actually tends to be lower than 32 °F.

upper limit for the temperature and a lower limit for the precipitation being established by present conditions in the area. However, because of precipitation on the lake surface, lake evaporation will be reduced to what is termed the *net evaporation*, the ideal relations between annual temperature, annual precipitation, and net evaporation shown in Fig.103. The evaporation rate derived by construction of the temperature march and hysteresis loop may then be considered a maximum for the lake surface.

A second possibility, once the maximum evaporation rate is established by the hysteresis loop, is to use the correlation of precipitation, runoff, and evaporation with the seasonal factor or distribution of the precipitation (Fig.100).

Assuming that a seasonal factor of unity (1.0) now exists in the area, and that the pluvial seasonal factor was not much different, the precipitation–evaporation and runoff–evaporation ratios can be figured. For instance, with a seasonal factor of 1.0 and an evaporation of 20 inches/year, a precipitation–evaporation ratio of 0.5 would indicate a precipitation of 10 inches/year with a corresponding runoff of 0.7 inches (Fig.100). Again, present runoff and precipitation establishes a lower limit. Since area of a lake in per cent of its drainage basin (LA') is generally known, the use of the equations even without previous determination of the evaporation rate, will give several combinations of precipitation, runoff, and evaporation which could have produced a lake of (LA') size. The only thing remaining for the investigator to do is to pinpoint which set of conditions most probably existed during the pluvial times of interest. However, if the evaporation rate and seasonal factor have been determined, and (LA') is known, figures for precipitation and runoff can be determined.

Certainly the previous method, as described, depends heavily on the derived temperature march of the area in question, thus if the march is in error significant discrepancies could be widely distributed. Palynology is now affording increased possibilities for checking derived temperature marches, providing that sufficient pollen of diagnostic species is present.

Perhaps it should be realized that it is not necessary for all of the climatic parameters to have changed since Pleistocene time. For instance, Pleistocene lakes may have been caused, in some areas, by only an increase in runoff due to cloudier days and/or cooler temperatures (decreased evaporation rate), rather than by a penecontemporaneous increase in precipitation and runoff. Such a circumstance was suggested by BRYAN (1950) for the New Mexico pluvial lakes, by CHARLESWORTH (1957) for parts of Europe, by GALLOWAY (1965) for parts of Australia, and most recently by the author (REEVES, 1965c) for the pluvial lake basins of the southern High Plains, Texas; however, new work (REEVES, 1966b) shows the improbability of runoff increasing enough, at least in the West Texas area.

SNYDER and LANGBEIN (1962) believe that the most probable precipitation–evaporation relationship exists where "... the product of the probability of a given change in evaporation by the probability of a corresponding change in precipitation ..." is maximum, or when:

$$\frac{Pc}{\delta p} = \frac{Ec}{\delta e}$$

where Pc is the change in precipitation, Ec is the change in evaporation, δp is the standard deviation of precipitation, and δe is the standard deviation of evaporation.

The most probable change in precipitation (Pc) then equals the change in evaporation (Ec) times the ratio of standard deviation of precipitation (δp) over standard deviation of evaporation (δe):

$$Pc = Ec \, \frac{\delta p}{\delta e}$$

and the most probable change in evaporation (Ec) equals the change in precipitation (Pc) times the ratio of standard deviation of evaporation (δe) over standard deviation of precipitation (δp):

$$Ec = Pc \, \frac{\delta e}{\delta p}$$

The preceding equations and methods may be used for the paleoclimatological investigation of any ancient lake basin, providing present weather conditions are known, and reasonably accurate maps of the area are available. Excellent results, using such methods, are in the literature for Lake Estancia, Mexico (LEOPOLD, 1951), Lake Bonneville, Utah (BROECKER and ORR, 1958), Spring Lake, Nevada (SNYDER and LANGBEIN, 1962), Gosuite Lake, Wyoming (BRADLEY, 1963), and for the pluvial lake basins of the southern High Plains (REEVES, 1965c, 1966b). LANGBEIN (1961) presents a thorough review of the principles of hydroclimatic investigation which should be reviewed by interested scientists.

It must be realized that not all of the pluvial lake basins of the world were closed, thus the discovery of an abandoned shoreline does not necessarily mean a

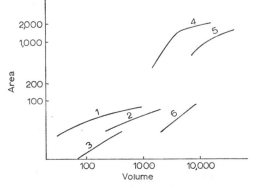

Fig.109. Graph of relation between lake area and volume of several of the world's closed lakes, area in thousands of acres, volume in thousands of acre-feet. 1 = Lake Corangamite, Australia; 2 = Owens Lake, California; 3 = Devils Lake, North Dakota; 4 = Lake Eyre, Australia; 5 = Great Salt Lake, Utah; 6 = Walker Lake, Nevada. (Modified after LANGBEIN, 1961.)

closed lake. SNYDER (1967) finds that 50% of the pluvial lakes in the classic Utah–Nevada–Oregon–southern California area were open, 30% of which spilled only at their highest water level. Establishment of an ancient lake level then does not necessarily mean that the lake achieved a climatic balance between evaporation from its surface and inflow from the surrounding basin, but perhaps that a balance existed between inflow, evaporation, and outflow. For this reason the search for an ancient spill point for each paleolake basin must be exhaustive for the accuracy of application of previous hydrologic formulas will depend on the presence or absence of a spill point and, if present, on its relative elevation and age to the lake basin.

Unfortunately there is no linear relation between the volume and area of most lakes (Fig.109) because of the varying length of time it takes for different lakes to reflect changes in volume. This can be seen in Fig.109 which shows the area-volume relations of several lakes. The volume (LV) of a closed lake is defined by the amount of inflow (LI) minus the amount of evaporation or outflow (LO), as:

$$LV = LI - LO$$

but since the outflow of the lake is equal to net evaporation (NE) times lake area (LA), the equation is:

$$LO = (NE)(LA)$$

LANGBEIN (1961) shows "outflow" of a closed lake also to be a function of the lake volume (LV) plus the constant b divided by the response time k, or the time it takes the lake to reflect a change in volume. Thus since k is defined as the change in lake volume (LV) divided by the change in lake discharge, or net evaporation for the closed basin (NE):

$$LO = (NE)(LA) = \frac{LV + b}{k}$$

TABLE XVII

LIST OF THE RESPONSE TIME (k) FOR THE LAKES SHOWN IN FIG.109

(Modified after LANGBEIN, 1961)

Lake	Response time (years)
Great Salt Lake, Utah	9
Walker Lake, Nevada	45
Lake Eyre, Australia	1.5
Lake Corangamite, Australia	10
Owens Lake, California	10
Devils Lake, North Dakota	14

A low response time, in the order of one year, is indicative of a typical playa lake (LANGBEIN, 1961) which immediately fills after a heavy rainfall. Lakes with high response periods, reacting very slowly to climatic changes, may then have shorelines out of phase with prevailing climatic conditions. Of course, there is a decided difference between the response factor for open and closed lakes, closed lakes generally having a longer response time than open lakes (LANGBEIN, 1961). The response factors for several of the world's best known lakes are listed in Table XVII.

PLANTS, COAL, SPORES, AND POLLEN STUDIES

In 1706 (LEIBNITZ) we find the first use of fossil plants as geologic indicators, but it was not until the period 1828–1837 that paleobotany, as such, was used by several Europeans, stratigraphic applications beginning with VON POST about 1916. Fossil fruits and seeds were used for determination of the Early Eocene climate of England (REID and CHANDLER, 1933), mainly fossil leaves for the Early Eocene of the Gulf Coast (BERRY, 1916), and fossil pollen for the Late Wisconsin climatic determinations for the southwestern United States (WENDORF, 1961; MARTIN, 1963a, 1963b; HESTER and SCHOENWETTER, 1964; OLDFIELD and SCHOENWETTER, 1964). Confirmation of southwestern climatic parameters derived by pollen analyses was later provided by paleohydrologic study (REEVES, 1965c, 1966b).

Most studies of fossil plants concern Tertiary (CHANEY, 1963) or older strata, often by investigation of coal measures. This is natural because coal is composed of plant debris; however, evidence indicates that some coal formed in much cooler climates than others, and of course, it is well known that present peat deposits are confined mainly to the mid to high latitudes.

Coal deposits require moisture, and are in fact prima facia evidence of very heavy precipitation, as well as a shallow basin whereby a swamp environment did develop. If the basin is too deep then lake conditions exist, at least until silting or filling reduces water depth where vegetation can take hold across the basin, the lake perhaps passing through the classical lake to bog/marsh to swamp sequence. Unfortunately few lacustrine coal deposits are known, the best example perhaps being the thin coals of old Gosiute Lake, Wyoming.

By far the most important, definitive paleolimnological studies, particularly from North America, are based on fossil plant remains and have dealt mainly with pollen. However, because spores generally coexist with pollen they likewise document past ecological changes and thereby offer an additional paleoclimatic study method. The study of spores and pollen, known as *palynology*, is the determination of past vegetation suites from the spores and/or pollen found in the sediments. Although initially used only for the Quaternary, palynology now has wide application even into the Paleozoic. The use of spores and of pollen to determine ancient vegetation proceeds on the premise that ancient plants (like today's) were environmentally controlled. Thus, study of present plants of like morphological character strongly suggests the character of ancient environmental conditions.

DEEVEY (1944) studied the Patzcuaro Lake sediments of central Mexico, proving the influence of pluvial climates at least 1,800 miles south of the glacial fronts and palynological studies of a core from Valle Grande, New Mexico, and of three cores from the Mexico City area (SEARS and CLISBY, 1952) illustrate a correlation of climatic alterations well south of the glacial front; thus even in areas not closely associated with the glaciers we know by only pollen studies that tremendous regional climatic changes occurred.

Palynology was first used in the desert southwest by LAUDERMILK and MUNZ (1934), but its use for paleolimnological investigation was prompted by SEARS (1952) and SEARS and CLISBY (1955). Since then pollen studies from cores taken from San Augustin (New Mexico), China Lake (California), Lake Bonneville (Utah), and Lake Cochise (Arizona), to name the more important, have established a rough outline of Pleistocene chronology in the American Southwest, based mainly on pine (*Pinus*) and spruce (*Picea*) profiles. Study of fungus spores (the oldest of which are of Pleistocene age) from several East African lakes has been underway for several years (WOLF 1966a,b; WOLF and CAVALIERE, 1966), but no direct application to Pleistocene lacustrine history is yet available. On the other hand, pollen studies have been or are now being conducted on such diverse lake basins as the Carolina Bays (FREY, 1953), the Texas peat bogs (POTZGER and THARP, 1943, 1947, 1954), Deadman Lake, New Mexico (BENT, 1960; BENT and WRIGHT, 1963), and the pluvial lake basins of West Texas most of which are or have yielded definitive Pleistocene data. Pollen studies giving very definitive paleoclimatic results have been made for several lake basins in the southwestern United States, including Lake San Augustin, New Mexico (CLISBY and SEARS, 1956), Searles, California (ROOSMA, 1958), and Cochise Lake, Arizona (HEVLY and MARTIN, 1961; MARTIN et al., 1961). Very accurate paleoclimatic data now exists for West Texas and eastern New Mexico, the result of HAFSTEN's (1961) pollen studies and the writer's (REEVES, 1965c, 1966a,b) investigations of paleohydrologic and paleowind conditions, the results of each study lending considerable authenticity to the other.

Determination of paleovegetation obviously gives a good indication of paleotemperatures. On the southern High Plains of Texas HAFSTEN (1961) found mainly pine and spruce pollen in Tahoka Clay strata (20,000–14,000 years B.P.), the pine suggesting a relatively dry but not even semi-arid, warm climate, and the spruce indicating a cold, perhaps wet, climate. Because spruce is now limited by the 21 °C (ca. 70 °F) average July isotherm and pine by the 10 °C (actually in the range 47 °–51 °F) summer isotherm (HELLAND, 1912; HAGEM, 1917; WENDORF, 1961), it becomes rather evident that unless the pollen was blown in, paleotemperatures on the southern High Plains of West Texas must have been less than about 70 °F during the warmest month (July?), but with a mean summer temperature not lower than about 50 °F. This means a minimum lowering of nearly 25 °F for the Pleistocene July temperature for West Texas.

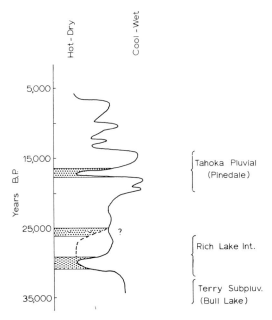

Fig.110. The pollen climatic curve for the southern High Plains, Texas, area, modified from WENDORF (1961) and OLDFIELD and SCHOENWETTER (1964). The terminology in parentheses is from the Rocky Mountain region. Stippled zones represent periods of carbonate deposition in West Texas pluvial lakes due to lake desiccation. Time scale based on uncorrected radiocarbon dates. (Modified from REEVES and PARRY, 1965.)

Similar evidence from other pollen studies from the southwestern United States is available. The lacustrine sediments below the present dry San Augustin plains of New Mexico show that spruce was widespread in the area until about 19,000 years B.P., and over in the Cochise Lake, Arizona, area, lacustrine sediments indicate a pine parkland 23,000–20,000 years B.P. (MALDE, 1964).

In general pollen analyses of lacustrine strata for different pluvial lake basins show that the pluvial climates in the southwestern United States were certainly wetter and colder than present conditions. Fig.110 illustrates, in a highly generalized fashion, the pollen-climatic curve for the southern High Plains, West Texas.

Although the above temperatures correlate closely with those determined for Lake Estancia, New Mexico (LEOPOLD, 1951; ANTEVS, 1954) ,and for several pluvial lake basins in the West Texas area (REEVES, 1965c, 1966b), considerable argument exists as to the type of vegetal cover. ANTEVS (1954) thinks the eastern New Mexico area was treeless but with tall grasses, WENDORF (1961), visualizes an open type forest, while both SAUER (1950) and STEWART (1953) think in terms of woodland. Because forest-produced soils are unknown in West Texas (REEVES, 1966a,b; WENDORF, 1961), I suspect that the trees were confined mainly to drainage valleys and areas immediately surrounding the lake basins.

Table XVIII shows the mean temperature calculated by both palynological

TABLE XVIII

SOME SUGGESTED CENOZOIC TEMPERATURES FOR THE UNITED STATES AND EUROPE (IN °C)[1]

	Europe	U.S. (Pacific)	U.S. (west central)
Recent			
Pliocene	10–14	5–8	10
Miocene	16–19	9–14	12
Oligocene	18–20	14–18	11–18
Eocene	20–22	18–25	18.5–20
Paleocene		14.5	18.5–25
Late Cretaceous		20	

[1] Compiled from data assembled by SCHWARZBACH (1961a, b), DORF (1955), WOLDSTEDT (1954), DURHAM (1950, and BUTZER (1964).

and zoological studies, of mainly the Cenozoic of Europe and the United States. The general drastic world-wide reduction of temperature is obvious.

Unfortunately several difficulties are inherent in palynology. First of all, a pollen analysis of a core does not in any way indicate the density or distribution of vegetal cover. Because of microscopic size (diameter of pollen grains range from about 0.01 to 0.1 mm) deposits are easily contaminated either by erosion and redeposition of sediments, by wind-borne pollen, or perhaps by water-distributed pollen; thus extreme caution must be exercised in extrapolating paleoclimatic parameters solely on the basis of palynology. Secondly, some species (*Pinus* or *Betula*) may be overly represented because of the great amount of pollen yielded by one tree, other species (*Quercus* or *Ulmus*) are under-represented because of poor pollen yield, and still other species (*Juniperus* or *Populus*) are seldom represented because of incompetent, rapidly decomposed pollen.

Pollen analyses (COLINVAUX, 1964) of Wisconsin-aged continental deposits (peat and soils) marginal to the Arctic Ocean suggest that the Arctic Basin was colder during Pleistocene time than at present and consequently *not* ice-free as suggested by EWING and DONN (1956, 1958). Palynological studies may then hold the possibility of widespread application to Pleistocene problems in general rather then simply revealing the paleofloras.

Diatoms, the siliceous shells of microscopic algae, have also been successfully used as climatic indicators (FJERDINGSTAD, 1954; ROUND, 1961; HOHN and HELLERMAN, 1961) being able to characterize flow of water and salt content from the Lubbock Lake Site, Lubbock, Texas.

VERTEBRATE AND INVERTEBRATE STUDIES

The Pleistocene faunas have been studied from Europe and Siberia to the Canadian Archapelago and the northern United States, the most complete knowledge coming from Europe (BUTZER, 1964) and the United States. In Europe the faunas are divided into a "cave fauna," a "steppe fauna," a "tundra fauna," an interglacial fauna and glacial fauna; however, such a complete definition is lacking in North America. Obviously, such a classification allows considerable paleoclimatic or paleo-environmental interpretation, for although the climatic interpretations are based on peculiarities of the animals caused by the climatic conditions, wide variations in geographic range of the different species exists.

In the United States there have been innumerable studies of the Pleistocene vertebrates, the remains of which have often been found in lacustrine exposures (Fig.111). The more important Pleistocene vertebrate studies are those of COPE (1892), HAY (1924, 1926), BARBOUR and SCHULTZ (1934), HIBBARD (1941), MEADE (1944) and DALQUEST (1962). The relations of Great Plains fauna and Pleistocene climatic change have been studied by HIBBARD (1944, 1949, 1960, 1963), TAYLOR (1960,

Fig.111. Fossil elephant leg bones in pumiceous sand of Fossil Lake, Oregon. Notice the breaks in both the tibia and femur. (Photo by I. S. Allison, by courtesy of I. S. Allison and Oregon State University Press.)

1965), and HIBBARD and TAYLOR (1960). FLINT (1957) lists the fossil Pleistocene vertebrates of North America, dividing into the three faunal zones.

The paleoclimatic importance of larger vertebrates is not as exact as other methods, hence environmental conditions should not be determined wholly on fossil faunas. Yet there is little argument that certain species seem to be ideal "thermometers." The woolly mammoth and woolly rhinoceros, with a 5-inch layer of fat, a 5-inch undercoat, and a generous sprinkling of longer-haired (12–25 inches) areas, were certainly not indicators of a warm climate, nor were the horses or deer diagnostic of the very cold areas.

Paleoclimatological studies may use several methods for paleoecological interpretations, one of the most obvious being the present geographic ranges of animals: in many parts of the world there exists endemic species that were apparently isolated by the Pleistocene climatic changes. The next most obvious method is perhaps the tolerant limits of the vertebrate's body. Reptiles, because they have no internal control over body temperature, naturally never exist (at least for long) in cold, frigid areas, yet they may inhabit areas where the temperature retreats below freezing for several months of the year by hibernating.

Morphological clues presented by animals are also of intense interest. Certainly, long fur, thick fat, and long hair are indicative of a cold climate; high crowned teeth of a grazing animal; and short crowned teeth of a forested environment (LUNDELIUS, 1964). Other methods concern the growth and condition of skeletal bones, associated faunas, and sediments, coprolites and biochemistry (LUNDELIUS, 1964).

One of the early principles used for mammalian fossil remains, particularly those of the elephants, mastodons, horses, and camels, was to mark the supposed Pleistocene–Recent boundary; however, zoologic geographic movements, in some instances, have suggested extinction. Extinction is now known to have taken place over many thousands of years (HESTER, 1960). Today mammalian remains are used to determine the extent of Pleistocene faunal shifts based, of course, on the premise that (1) present climates are radically different from Pleistocene climates and, (2) that fossil faunas were as environmentally controlled as living contemporaries. Thus, in the state of Texas, we see a decided disappearance in northern mammalian species beginning about 9,500 years B.P. and continuing until, by 7,000 B.P. only present mammals existed. (SLAUGHTER and HOOVER, 1963).

Invertebrates, particularly gastropods, mollusks, and ostracods, have been of greater paleoecologic use to paleolimnologists than the vertebrates, probably because of better preservation and more extensive occurrence, but were apparently slower to adapt to climatic changes (CHEATUM et al., 1966).

In the United States, F. C. BAKER (1920) made an early study of mollusks in the Great Lakes region, and recently ROSCOE (1963) summarized the mollusca of the Bonneville Basin, and intensive studies of the crustacean Cladoceran fauna have been made in Germany, Denmark, England, and throughout the central United States. Perhaps the most interesting, best detailed invertebrate studies concern those of the High Plains, particularly of the West Texas area (FRYE and LEONARD, 1957a; TAYLOR,

1960; ALLEN and CHEATUM 1961; WENDORF, 1961; CHEATUM and ALLEN, 1963, 1965; CHEATUM et al., 1966; among others), in the southwestern Kansan-northwestern Oklahoma area (TAYLOR, 1960, 1965) and in Ohio (LAROQUE, 1966).

The molluscan collections from the West Texas area indicate an average July temperature of about 70 °F and an average January temperature of about 25 ° to 30 °F during Late Wisconsin pluvial times (WENDORF, 1961). Although these figures are a bit different from those derived by the use of hydrologic methods (REEVES, 1965c, 1966b), they are collaborative in proving radically lower pluvial temperatures. Certain mollusca are also indicative of depositional environments. For instance, *Physa anatina*, *Gyraulus parvus*, and *Stagnicola caperata* suggest quiet shallow water with abundant vegetation and *Sphaerium striatinum* and *Pisidium nitidum* are indicative of clear flowing perennial rivers or creeks. Thus invertebrate studies combined with palynological and hydrologic and hydroclimatic results may reveal an amazingly accurate picture of past environments.

The use of marine invertebrates as depositional temperature indicators by study of oxygen isotope ratios, although not as yet directly applicable to most paleolimnological studies, is discussed in the section on Geochemical studies (p.166).

SOIL STUDIES

Much of the history of ancient lake basins, and particularly their past extent, may in many cases be quickly determined by soil studies (MORRISON, 1964a,b). In general, semi-arid areas, because of a scarcity of water and only intermittent chemical weathering, develop poor soils consisting of a thin A-zone over incompletely disintegrated, oxidized parent material. Areas of internal drainage may exhibit lenses of the common salts, the soils showing well-developed Sa or Ca zones.

The major problem in working with soils is to distinguish between a *relict* or an *exhumed* soil. Soil development in pluvial lake basins is often of the relict type, in that the soil formed on the old basin floor but has not been subsequently buried; however, some basin soils may be exhumed by erosion of overlying lacustrine strata. Other basin soils are of Recent age.

Successive soil development from lacustrine strata around present lake playas is well exhibited on the southern High Plains, Texas, and New Mexico, these soils known as *Calcisols* (HARPER, 1957) since they develop from parent material rich in calcium carbonate. The Calcisols of the West Texas area are known as the Arch, Church, Gomez, Mansker, and Portales, the Arch being the most immature. Thus, excluding the present lake beds (Randall Clay), and Recent deflation products (Drake Sand), the pluvial lake basins on the southern High Plains, because of their progressive decrease in size with age, are encircled by bands of progressively older soils. The arcuate shape and position of ancient dune trends, which mark past playa levels and tend to separate the different soils, show particularly well (Fig.112).

Soils in the West Texas area, developed during each Pleistocene interpluvial, are apparently capped by caliche, optimum conditions for caliche formation being 15–25 inches of rainfall and a mean annual temperature of 50–55° F (FRYE and LEONARD, 1967), thus in many areas several caliche profiles exist. Soils, developed during Pleistocene interpluvial times, in many areas of the United States can be used as a basis for Pleistocene stratigraphic studies. Little is known about the Afton and Yarmouth soils, the most complete works probably being by FRYE and LEONARD (1952), but the Sangamon soil is considered a prime stratigraphic horizon from Ohio into southwestern Texas (FRYE and LEONARD, 1965). This remarkable continuity occurs because of: (*1*) the characteristic position of the Sangamon soil above the Loveland Loess in Kansas, (*2*) a distinctive clayey B-horizon, and (*3*) a well-developed caliche zone.

The Wisconsin loess, which covers much of the central interior of the United States (Fig.113) exhibits two paleosoils (the Farmdale and Brady) in the Iowa–Kansas–Nebraska area (FRYE and LEONARD, 1952, 1965; FRYE and WILLMAN, 1960). Development is weak in the West Texas pluvial area although FRYE and LEONARD (1965) suspect an occurrence in the Lake Lomax vicinity of Howard and Martin Counties.

Fig.112. The southeast part of pluvial Lake Rich basin, Terry County, Texas, showing progressive older age of sand dunes, based on soil studies, away from the playa. The *I* dunes were formed during the last 5,000 years, the *II* were formed sometime in the period 14,000–7,000 years B. P., and those marked *III* were formed over 21,000 years B.P.

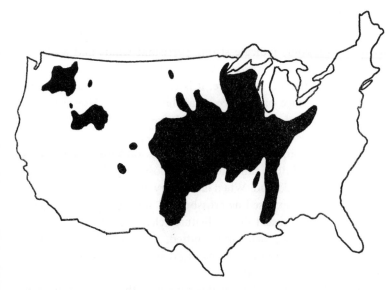

Fig.113. Highly generalized map of loess distribution in the United States, mainly of Wisconsin age. (Modified after THORP et al., 1952.)

The development of a soil type depends greatly on climate, parent material, topography, and time. Therefore, because parent material, time, and topography are well known for the Pleistocene soils they are indicators of paleoclimate even though climate intensity still exists as an important variable. Basically *pedalfer* soils indicate temperate, forested areas, *pedocal* soils warm, dry grasslands, and the *laterites* a tropical environment; the soils of pluvial lake areas throughout the world are principally pedocals, those of the glaciated or near-glacial areas being pedalfers.

Certainly red to yellow soils, because of their high concentration of iron oxides, suggest a warm, humid, oxidizing climate, and light gray to white, calcified soils indicate a warm, dry climate. However, caution must be exercised when using soils for the deduction of past climatic events because development results from the intricate variability of innumerable factors such as topography, ground water, time, rainfall, and temperature to mention only a few. Soil color has been inferred by many investigators (THORP et al., 1951; SIMONSON, 1954; CARTER, 1956) as an indicator of either past climate or soil age, the reds and yellows indicating a warm, dry climate with the soil becoming redder with age. Such generalizations may be adequate for local areas and restricted use, but are obviously dangerous for proper scientific evaluation.

Most soils found in pluvial lake basins are *calcified* (i.e., pedocals) in that there is an accumulation of solubles, usually the carbonates, because of an absence of leaching. This condition is more pronounced within the basin than in the surrounding area soils because the lacustrine strata are themselves characteristically initially rich in carbonates.

WIND STUDIES

Aeolian sandstones or sands indicate strong persistant winds and a plentiful supply of clastics, both of which may exist in a hot dry climate, a hot humid climate, or a cold damp or cold arid climate. Therefore, it is extremely difficult to interpret paleoclimates only on the presence or absence of aeolian features. However, when correlated with palynological and/or hydrologic evidence, the climatic conditions become definitive.

Immediate recognition of ancient dunes is sometimes difficult, but FRIEDMAN (1962) found that recent river and dune sands tend to be positively skewed and recent beach sands tend to be negatively skewed. When laboratory analyses are not available ancient aeolian sand dunes, now exposed as crossbedded sandstones, can generally be recognized by comparison to present dunes, features characteristic of both being a very high percentage of rounded, well-sorted, pitted, and frosted quartz grains. Wind direction is measured by the dip directions of cross-strata on the lee faces of the dunes, barchan dunes being preferred.

Paleowind directions have been determined for many of the aeolian sandstones of Pennsylvanian, Permian (REICHE, 1938; POOLE, 1963) and Triassic (POOLE, 1961, 1962, 1963) age in the western United States. The directions of Pleistocene paleowinds have been determined by study of sand dunes in Nebraska (SMITH, 1964), Kansas (SMITH, 1938, 1940), Arizona (HACK, 1941), eastern New Mexico and the Texas panhandle (F. A. MELTON, 1940), and on the southern High Plains of Texas (PRICE, 1958; REEVES, 1965d) (Fig.114). A vast amount of literature concerning dune studies from various parts of the world also exists, some of the more important being on the aeolian features of Peru (SIMONS, 1956), Arabia (HOLM, 1953), Central Asia (HEDIN,

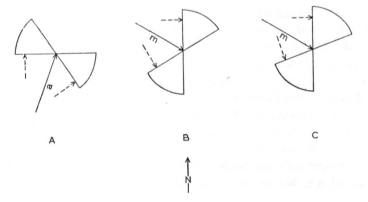

A   B   C

↑
N

Fig.114. Plot of the main trend of the three major dune series associated with pluvial lake basins on the southern High Plains, Texas. The solid arrows represent the average (a) or mean (m) dune-producing wind directions, the dashed short arrows represent the end directions from each average or mean. A. Dunes formed approximately during the last 5,000 years, mainly during Alti-thermal time, by winds blowing N 20°E. B. Dunes formed before Altithermal time but after the last major desiccation of the West Texas pluvial lakes, by winds blowing S60°E. C. Dunes formed before the last major filling of the West Texas lakes (21,000–14,000 years B.P.), by winds blowing S60°E.

1904), Turkestan (FEDOROVICH, 1940), Australia (MADIGAN, 1936; GALLOWAY, 1965), Hungary (HOGBOM, 1923), India (CORNISH, 1897), Gascony (DUREGNE, 1904), and Africa (MACKENZIE, 1946; GROVE, 1958; SMITH, 1963).

Although studying ancient aeolian features reveals only the paleowind direction, the source of the sand particles and often the location of the aeolian belt provides many environmental clues. The Pennsylvanian–Permian aeolian sand belt of the Colorado Plateau occurs between definite marine and continental facies, thus is interpreted as a coastal-plain dune complex (REICHE, 1938), related evaporatic rocks indicating a hot arid climate. The Wingate Sandstone, occurring within the fluvial to lacustrine Chinle Formation, indicates a hot, dry environment, but with nearby areas of considerable runoff (POOLE, 1963).

Determination of the source for the clastics and the paleowind directions, from study of present or Pleistocene dunes, is naturally less subject to error than determinations from ancient sandstones. Paleolimnologists are particularly interested in paleowind directions to see if they have shaped the lake basin(s) or in the source of the clastics which may pinpoint a deflating playa. The great pluvial lakes of the western United States and Mexico frequently have associated areas of extensive aeolian debris, the clastics generally originating by deflation of the present playas. Every large pluvial lake basin in West Texas exhibits several sand dune trends marking old abandoned lake and playa levels (Fig.112). Evaluation of these dunes reveals not only the trend, extent, and developmental histories of the basins, but a new paleowind direction which existed across the area during late Wisconsin time (REEVES, 1965d). The Pleistocene paleowind directions for the central and southern High Plains, as documented by aeolian features, are shown in Fig.114.

Probably the best example of aeolian deposition occurring on the lee side of a large pluvial lake basin are the Medaños de Samalayuca of Northwestern Chihuahua, Mexico. This vast area of aeolian dunes, some of which are over 300 ft. high, exists because of the prevailing westerlies which deflate the playa of recently discovered pluvial Lake Palomas (REEVES, 1965b). Unfortunately dune chronology is not known, but the older winds are expected to pre-date the Wisconsin.

SEA-LEVEL MOVEMENT STUDIES

Pleistocene sea-level fluctuations have been studied by many investigators (FISK and MCFARLAN, 1955; SHEPARD and SUESS, 1956; EMERY, 1958; CURRAY, 1960, 1961, 1965; FAIRBRIDGE, 1961b; MCFARLAN, 1961; DONN et al., 1962; SCHOLL, 1964; STEPHENS and SYNGE, 1966; SCHOLL and STUIVER, 1967), yet, only rather generalized results are safely inferred. All evidence indicates that sea-level movements were synchronous with glacial chronology, sea level being about 1,246 ft. higher than the present at the start of Pliocene time (ZEUNER, 1959) and falling progressively during the Pleistocene, large falls occurring during the glacial stages and rises occurring during interglacial stages. DONN et al. (1962) show a maximum Wisconsin lowering of about

438 ft. and a maximum Illinoian lowering of about 450 ft., but widespread sub-merged sea cliffs, terraces, and Pleistocene fossils now indicate a Wisconsin lowering of about −600 ft. (R. F. Dill, personal communication, 1967).

Fig.115 shows the sea-level curve as compiled by McFARLAN (1961) which more or less matches that of other investigators of the last few years (SHEPARD and SUESS, 1956; CURRAY, 1960, 1961; JELGERSMA and PANNEKOEK, 1960). Of most interest is the last recorded low stand at approximately 19,000 years B.P., and the relative stability during the last 5,000 years. The oceanic low-stand correlates with the period of deposition (Woodfordian substage) of extensive pluvial lake deposits throughout the western states: the Tahoka Formation of West Texas; the Bonneville Formation of Utah and the Sehoo Formation of Nevada. The periods of desiccation occurring about 17,000 and 14,000 years B.P. (REEVES and PARRY, 1965) are also particularly well recorded throughout the western pluvial lake province, both by pollen profiles and deposition of carbonates (WENDORF, 1961; OLDFIELD and SCHOENWETTER, 1964; REEVES and PARRY, 1965; REEVES, 1966a).

No great eustatic change has apparently taken place during the last 5,000–6,000 years although considerable oscillation of the order of about 2 meters has occurred (BLOCH, 1965), SCHOLL and STUIVER (1967) believing sea level stabilized in the period 3,000–5,000 years B.P. These small, repetitive movements, well re-corded by various investigators (J. IVES, 1803; PIRENNE, 1958; KOSTER, 1960; CLARKE, 1960; KESTNER, 1962), are thought to have resulted from albedo changes of polar ice caps produced by loess and from volcanic dust (BLOCH, 1965).

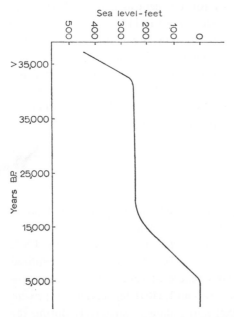

Fig.115. Elevation of sea level in the last 35,000 years as determined by radiocarbon dates from the Mississippi River delta. Before 35,000 years B.P. sea level was at least −450 feet. (After McFARLAN, 1961.)

Perhaps the best clue to the actual amount of Pleistocene lacustrine water is given by the discrepancy between ice volume and Wisconsin sea level. ERICSON and WOLLIN (1964) place Wisconsin sea level at −180 m (590 ft.), a figure substantiated by submarine rocky terraces, sea cliffs, and fossil evidence from several widely separated geographic areas (R. F. Dill, personal communication 1967); however, computations of Wisconsin ice volume indicate a maximum lowering of only about 480 ft. Thus, there is at least 110 ft. of ocean rise for which we cannot account by ice volume. This, I think, most vividly shows that, assuming estimations of ice volume to be near-correct, there were many more pluvial lakes throughout the world and that there was probably much more water in our recognized lake basins and near-surface aquifers than we presently suspect.

ARCHEOLOGICAL STUDIES

Many of the most startling archeological finds of the southwestern United States have been intimately associated with paleodrainage or paleolake basins (SAYLES and ANTEVS, 1941; SELLARDS, 1952; GROSSCUP, 1956; MORRISON, 1958; WENDORF and HESTER, 1962; GREEN, 1962, 1963, 1964; MEHRINGER and HAYNES, 1965). For instance the well-known Clovis, Blackwater Draw, and Lubbock Lake Early Man sites are associated with Pleistocene fluviatile features (GREEN, 1962, 1963, 1964), the ancient cultures of the Great Basin, through California and into Baja California and old Mexico (POURADE, 1966), and even archaic remains are best found within old lake basins and around present playas. In fact, of over 50 sites on the southern High Plains of West Texas, 30 were near stream channels, fourteen near ponds, ten on dunes adjacent to ponds, and one on a stream terrace (WENDORF and HESTER, 1962). Obviously the lake basins, even during climatic periods of drought, attracted the life-sustaining animal herds because of intermittent water, peripheral springs, and salt deposits. Thus, Early Man, rather than wandering in pursuit of game, apparently learned to rest and live on the shores of lakes and streams, close both to food and water.

Nowhere is the relation between old lakes and man more dramatically illustrated than by the pollen studies from Lake Texcoco, central Mexico. During the wet, moist period 4,000–2,500 years B.P., the Archaic, maize-growing culture flourished along the Lake Texcoco shores, but desiccation soon forced following cultures away from the lake and to areas of more plentiful moisture.

Although the relation of man and extinct species is not known in the northeastern United States (GRIFFIN, 1965), several sites in the southwestern part of the country clearly indicate a contemporary association. Bison, mammoth, tapir, and horse remains were associated with artifacts at the Lehner site, Arizona (ANTEVS, 1959; LANCE, 1959), several points were found with elephant bone at Sandia Cave, New Mexico (GREEN, 1962), and points were found with mammoth remains at the Clovis, New Mexico, site (GREEN, 1962). The interesting thing about this association is that Early Man and the Late Pleistocene megafauna existed when the climate was cooler and moister than at present (GREEN, 1962, 1963; MARTIN, 1963a,b; MEHRINGER and HAYNES, 1965; REEVES, 1965c, 1966b), the megafauna becoming extinct and the cultures disappearing when the southwestern environment became semi-arid to arid (RUSSELL, 1885; ALBRITTON and BRYAN, 1939; LEOPOLD, 1951; HUNT, 1953; HAURY, 1960). Thus *if* extinction of both large mammals and the Early Man cultures was due to a drastic climatic change, paleolimnological studies should be of decided interest to the anthropologists and archaeologists.

GEOCHEMICAL STUDIES

The obvious application of geochemistry to paleolimnological studies concerns absolute age determinations. Unfortunately since the lacustrine sections are sedimentary the number of applicable radioactive methods is severely limited, but continued new developments hold the promise of the development of more than one method which will yield universally acceptable results. Early dating of Pleistocene events depended on inexact and short-span methods such as weathering of glacial fills and associated delta building (KAY, 1931), rhythmite counting (DE GEER, 1912, 1940), and the counting of tree growth rings, or dendrochronology (DOUGLASS, 1919).

One of the earliest methods of dating lacustrine deposits was by the counting of "varves." The term *varve*, from the Swedish *varv* (a periodic repetition), was suggested for layers of lacustrine strata representing one year's sedimentation (DE GEER, 1912); however, the term *rhythmite* (DE GEER, 1940; SMILEY et al., 1955) is most popular today, particularly when working lacustrine strata well removed from the glacial fronts. Discovery of rhythmites in a lacustrine section, which may consist of alterations of lithology, texture, accessory minerals, or amount of organic debris, immediately creates the problem of true time length per depositional unit which may often be determined by pollen counts and fossils. Once this is established simple counting and multiplication gives an age for the rhythmite sequence and a minimum age for the basin.

Varved deposits are and were produced mainly in proglacial lakes, the coarser suspended sands and clays settling during the summer, the finer debris not settling until the lake calms beneath winter ice. Unfortunately, only varves left by the last glacial retreat show any consistent correlation from lake basin to lake basin and thus are the only ones available for chronological interpretation. However, caution must be exercised in using varves because varve sequences can be created, in shallow lakes, by local storms.

By counting varves, extending back about 17,000 years B.P., DE GEER (1912, 1940) followed the progressive retreat of Sweden's last ice sheet and ANTEVS (1925), by the same method, developed a glacial chronology extending back about 28,000 years for parts of eastern Canada, yet considerable interpolation was necessary. Radiocarbon dates have indicated that much of Antevs interpolation was incorrect, but ANTEVS (1957) questions the validity of the dates, suggesting the older dates are progressively too young. ANTEVS (1957) finds good correlation of varve chronology from North America to Europe.

[14] Carbon

Starting in about 1940, and particularly during the period 1955–1965, several methods utilizing radioactive isotopes were developed for securing absolute Pleistocene dates, most resulting from research studies at or associated with the Lamont Geological Observatory, Palisades, New York. Most of the various methods were primarily for use with marine sediments, but some are applicable to lacustrine studies. The methods of most use to paleolimnology, with applicable comments, are shown in Table XIX.

TABLE XIX

ISOTOPIC DATING METHODS MOST APPLICABLE TO PALEOLIMNOLOGICAL STUDIES

Isotope method	Range in 1,000 years	Remarks
[14]C	0–40	used on a wide range of organics and carbonate rocks
[230]Th	0–200	as above
[4]He		used on mollusks, coral remains
[40]Ar		used on volcanics

The first ^{14}C age determinations were reported in the late 1940's and early 1950's (LIBBY et al., 1949; LIBBY, 1951, 1952, 1955; ARNOLD and LIBBY, 1951; KULP et al., 1951; ARNOLD and LIBBY, 1951). Many of the dates, when compared to archaeological and/or stratigraphic evidence seemed in error, therefore possibilities and probabilities for error were examined by several investigators (ANTEVS, 1953; HUNT, 1955; BROECKER and KULP, 1956; BROECKER and ORR, 1958).

The ^{14}C method assumes that: (1) original ^{14}C content is known; (2) the ^{14}C content has been altered only by natural disintegration; and (3) ^{14}C is the only C isotope measured. Fortunately the gas-filled proportional counters have eliminated the possibilities of atmospheric contamination which became serious by 1958 when $4.8 \cdot 10^{27}$ [14]C atoms were found in the atmosphere due to atomic bomb detonation (GIBBS, 1962), and refined laboratory techniques generally eliminate measurement error; however, the amount of ^{14}C in the atmosphere has undoubtedly varied throughout geologic time and is certainly known to have varied in the last few thousand years (DAMON et al., 1965). Dating of tree rings representing the last 24,000–26,000 years, indicates that atmospheric fluctuation of ^{14}C lowers ages of samples older than 2,000 years, the increase in atmospheric ^{14}C being about 0.4%/100 years (SCHELL et al., 1965). BROECKER and WALTON (1959) find radiocarbon dates from Lakes Lahontan and Bonneville about 500 years too great due to a lower $^{14}C/^{12}C$ ratio in the lake than in the atmosphere at the time of carbonate precipitation.

The general method followed for ^{14}C dating by a central wire counter is conversion of the sample to CO_2 which is then purified, pressurized, and counted. The maximum assignable age of the sample depends on the fewest counts recorded over and above the background level which, (P. H. Monagham, written communication, 1965), for most wire counters, is about 37,000 years. The radiocarbon half-life used may range from 5,568 $\pm$ 30 years as established by LIBBY (1955), to 5,700 established by the National Bureau of Standards in 1961 to 5,730 years as determined by GOODWIN (1962), although a half-life of 5,833 $\pm$ 127 years was calculated from Sequoia (*giganitea*) rings (SCHELL et al., 1965). Today the use of gas-filled proportional counters and liquid scintillation counting, using benzene, methane (Diethorn, 1956), acetylene (CRATHORN, 1953), carbon dioxide (FERGUSSON, 1955), or ethane (GEYH, 1965) may give ages to about 65,000 years B.P. (DE VRIES, 1959), but most laboratories lose confidence beyond about 40,000 year B.P. dates.

Three possible methods of alteration of ^{14}C concentration in sediments after removal from the CO_2 cycle are known: (*1*) the extraction of one carbon isotope relative to another (*fractionation*); (*2*) exchange of carbon atoms between sample and surrounding materials (*exchange*); and (*3*) micro- and/or macroadditions of older or younger carbonaceous materials (*intrusion*). Research (LIBBY, 1952, 1955; BROECKER and KULP, 1956) indicates effects of fractionation and exchange are negligible for both organic and inorganic carbonate *unless* recrystallization occurs.

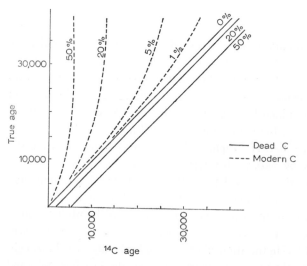

Fig.116. Curves showing how various per cents of dead and contemporary carbon effect the derived radiocarbon age. (Modified after BROECKER and KULP, 1956.)

Many pluvial lake basins are either underlaid or surrounded by older carbonate rocks, with present playas surrounded by outcrops of older lacustrine strata; therefore, possibilities of contamination by intrusion of older carbonate do exist and have been observed (Fig.64).

Fig.116 illustrates error in true age caused by intrusion of dead and/or contemporary carbon. Old carbon, at least up to about 20%, has little percentage effect on samples over 20,000 years but as true age is reduced percentage contamination increases for a set percentage of dead carbon. Thus, contemporary samples, if contaminated by 20% dead carbon, will give a ^{14}C date of about 2,000 years, but a sample of true age 30,000 years would only show a ^{14}C age of about 32,000 years. However, as Fig.116 shows, as the true age of the sample increases the greater and greater becomes the discrepancy between true and radiocarbon age, particularly for very high percentages of contemporary carbon contamination.

OLSON (1963) finds the true age of a sample contaminated by a known percentage of dead carbon by the formula:

$$e^{-tm/8030} = fe^{-tc/8030} + (1-f)e^{-ts/8030}$$

where t_s is true age, f the fraction of dead carbon, t_m the apparent age, and t_c the age of the contaminant (BROECKER and KAUFMAN, 1965).

The rate of contamination by intrusion of old carbon supplied by surrounding older lake sediments during pluvial times is conjectural, but worth considering since such contamination presently occurs (Fig.64). Many pluvial basins, especially in West Texas, were apparently surrounded by well-forested shores of grass and trees (WENDORF, 1961; OLDFIELD and SCHOENWETTER, 1964; REEVES, 1965c, 1966b), so possibilities of considerable quantities of dead carbon reaching the playas by sheet wash may have been more remote than expected. In areas where little vegetation existed runoff could have transported considerable dead carbon to the playa. Certainly spread of pluvial lake waters over older lacustrine strata and extension of incipient pluvial lake playas by wave and end-current erosion into older lake deposits, as well as material washed into playas before pluvial vegetation took hold, would have contaminated certain horizons. Whether such horizons would be preserved, mixed, diluted, and selectively deposited in the basin or carried downstream by an effluent is unknown.

Another source of possible error for radiocarbon dates from lacustrine strata concerns the ^{14}C/^{12}C ratios of the ancient lake water. Generally ^{14}C/^{12}C ratios for separate lakes varies greatly because of differences in concentration of carbonate brought to the lakes by different influents and that removed by different effluents, as well as by different exchange ratios between lake water carbonate and the atmosphere (BROECKER and ORR, 1958). However, if several lakes are part of a vigorous open lake system the ^{14}C concentration of the shared drainage, and thus of the lakes, would be expected to be very near, if not at, atmospheric equilibrium. Some exchange of ^{14}C from atmosphere to lacustrine strata during periods of desiccation may occur, but errors would be inconsequential except for playa surface samples whose age exceeds about 25,000 years. Atmospheric contamination errors in samples younger than 25,000 years average only about 3–4% (BROECKER and ORR, 1958). The original ^{14}C content of carbon in ancient plants, shells, and bone is never more than $\pm 3\%$ that in modern wood (CRAIG, 1954; BROECKER and KULP, 1956); however, shells, marl, or vegetation from closed lakes which derive water from underlying ancient carbonates generally exhibit a ^{14}C deficiency (DEEVEY, et al., 1954). Maximum deficiencies, which may cause an 1800-year error (BROECKER and KULP, 1956), will give a ^{14}C age of 3,600 years for a sample actually only 1800 years old. However, as actual sample age increases percentage error in the ^{14}C age decreases; at an actual age of 20,000 years an error of only about 9% exists.

Various materials, all of which may be found in lacustrine strata, can be used to secure radiocarbon dates; however, each exhibits variations in ^{14}C content to modern materials and different possibilities for error. This is summarized in Table XX. Radiocarbon dates from most lacustrine strata are determined by measuring ^{14}C concentration from either a carbonate fraction, a sample of carbonate rock, or an organic fraction. Secondary organic solubles (humic acid) and carbonates are readily removed from the organic fraction by a dilute acid-bath (OLSON and BROECKER 1958), thus organic dates are reliable providing no additions have occurred. Because transfer of carbon from ground water bicarbonate to carbonate strata is remote (LIBBY, 1952; BROECKER and KULP, 1956) except during recrystallization, and

TABLE XX

MATERIALS OFTEN ASSOCIATED WITH THE LACUSTRINE ENVIRONMENT WHICH CAN BE USED FOR RADIOCARBON DATING WITH PERTINENT RELATIVE DATA

Dateable materials	Average amount needed (g)	Remarks	Source
Bones	100	Carbon content low, easily contaminated	Pleistocene vertebrates
Carbonate rock	50	Contamination generally observable in thin section	Lacustrine limestones and dolomites
Carbonate: disseminated	50	Contamination serious	Lacustrine clays, etc.
Charcoal	10	Carbon content high	Old campfires, forest fires
Peat: organic zones	20	Carbon content high	Swamps, old springs
Shells	50	Contamination easily determined, but carbonate source must be known	Invertebrates, mainly mollusca
Wood	20	Generally not well preserved in playa areas May be found in dune areas	Ancient trees, vegetation

because soluble organics and surface contaminating carbonates are removed by acid, primary lacustrine carbonates give reliable dates, *providing* no intrusion or recrystallization has occurred. Radiocarbon dates based on carbonate fractions obviously are not reliable.

Lacustrine carbonates may also give anomalous dates if containing ^{14}C derived from surrounding vegetation. Radiocarbon dates on caliche, from ground water, or from terrestrial snails are generally anomalous due to dilution of the carbonate with plant-derived carbon. This may be determined by the $^{13}C/^{12}C$ ratio and corrected by the equation:

$$P = \left(\frac{pl}{pl + ls} \right)$$

where *pl* equals derived carbon and *ls* equals limestone derived carbon (PEARSON, 1965), providing no isotopic exchange has occurred. Fresh-water or continental environments tend to be enriched in isotopically light carbon, thus fresh-water carbonates are usually in the range $\delta\ ^{13}C$ -2 to $-12\%_0$ while their marine counterparts range from -2 to $+4\%_0$ (M. L. Keith, personal communication, 1962). Carbonates deposited in saline lakes should have $\delta\ ^{13}C$ ratios in the marine range. This is well illustrated by evaporative dolomites from the West Texas lakes with $\delta\ ^{13}C$ ranging from $+5.8$ to -3.1, the freshwater limestones from Guthrie Lake, Lynn County, Texas, and calcite from Mound Lake, Texas, ranging from -4.8 to -3.6.

The reliability of ^{14}C dates, after initial errors were discovered, has long been questioned and considered, and rather transparent manipulation of dates not fitting preconceived stratigraphic pictures have often resulted. Fortunately today we know that contamination by young carbon in organics over 40,000 years old and in carbonates over 20,000 years old, as well as dates from terrestrial materials, may be in error (BROECKER, 1965), thus dating results must be interpreted with this in mind. Reliability is naturally best tested in any area by multiple dates: (*1*) on the same sample(s); (*2*) on definite stratigraphic correlations; (*3*) on known stratigraphic succession; and (*4*) on contemporary samples.

Uranium methods

BARNES et al., (1956) discovered that the $^{230}Th/^{232}Th$ ratio in marine carbonate (coral) was, like the ratio of $^{12}C/^{14}C$, a time function, but the ^{230}Th method did not become accurate until after refinements suggested by THURBER (1962). Comparison with ^{14}C dates (THURBER et al., 1965; KAUFMAN and BROECKER, 1965) and the half-life of ^{230}Th of 75,200 years (ATTREE et al., 1962) indicates that ^{230}Th dates are particularly reliable in the period 10,000–200,000 years. Although GOLDBERG and GRIFFIN (1964) show that ^{230}Th ages may be in error by a factor of 10, comparison of ^{14}C and ^{230}Th dates from carbonates of Lakes Lahontan and Bonneville generally show good agreement (BROECKER and KAUFMAN, 1965).

The $^{230}Th/^{232}Th$ method, which is based on the ratio change between the isotopes, assumes that: (*1*) the samples have received no additional U or Th, or (*2*) that any external ^{230}Th added to the sample is reliably revealed by the ^{232}Th content as suggested by TATSUMOTO and GOLDBERG (1959). The amount of ^{226}Ra, produced by ^{230}Th, also presents a method of checking ^{230}Th presence, thus when ^{226}Ra and ^{232}Th amounts are in line with ^{230}Th presence, the dates secured are assumed correct (BROECKER, 1965). SACKETT (1960) suggested that the ^{231}Pa/^{230}Th ratio would give reliable dates, at least up to about 120,000 years B.P., recent study (SACKETT, 1965) showing the protactinium–ionium ages within 30% of radiocarbon dates from the same cores. Unfortunately considerable difficulty has occurred with the ionium–thorium method because of migration of ionium in the sediments.

The 250,000 year half-life of ^{234}U also seems ideal for Pleistocene dating but studies (BROECKER and KAUFMAN, 1965; KAUFMAN and BROECKER, 1965) indicate that, as for most of the uranium methods, the lacustrine environment is generally too variable to allow a reasonable estimate of the excess ^{234}U in the datable lacustrine carbonates.

4 Helium

FANALE and SCHAEFFER (1965) derived absolute dates from aragonitic Tertiary fossils by examination of the helium–uranium ratio, of course assuming that parent uranium, once incorporated in the shell, was not subsequently exchanged and that helium found in the shell represents all and only that helium arising from the uranium disintegration. Dates on the same fossils by the ^{230}Th/^{234}U method, as well as stratigraphic evidence, indicate a high degree of accuracy except when contamination of the fossil by additional uranium occurs. This method, although not limited by a short half-life, is dependent on presence of unaltered fossil mollusks which contain uranium.

^{40}*Potassium–*^{40}*Argon*

EVERNDEN et al. (1964) found unusual agreement between potassium–argon dates from Tertiary volcanic tuffs and stratigraphic age of associated Tertiary mammals. Unfortunately this method, to date, is of limited use to the paleolimnologist because required volcanics, other than volcanic ash, are seldom found associated with lacustrine strata. Secondly, the lower limit of about 1 million years excludes most of the Pleistocene sections.

^{18}O/^{16}O *ratio; boron analyses*

The shells of certain marine invertebrates have been found to accurately record depositional water temperatures (EMILIANI, 1955b; PARKER, 1958; ERICSON et al., 1961; ERICSON, 1961); thus, depositional temperatures throughout most of post-Silurian time[1] have been determined by oxygen isotope study (Table XXI). Early

---

[1] Pre-Devonian fossils have generally experienced alteration of their original oxygen isotope atoms.

TABLE XXI

ABBREVIATED LIST OF REFERENCES TO OXYGEN ISOTOPE STUDIES FOR DETERMINATION OF
PALEOTEMPERATURES OF THE DIFFERENT GEOLOGIC PERIODS

Geologic time period	Principal references
Recent	EPSTEIN and LOWENSTAM (1953), BOWEN (1966)
Pleistocene	EMILIANI (1954a, 1955a), VALENTINE and MEADE (1960, 1961), ERICSON et al. (1961)
Tertiary	EMILIANI and EDWARDS (1953), EMILIANI (1956, 1961), LONGINELLI and TOGLIATTI (1962), BOWEN and FRITZ (1963)
Cretaceous	UREY et al. (1951), LOWENSTAM and EPSTEIN (1954), BOWEN (1961a, b, c, d, 1963), BOWEN and FONTES (1963), NAIDIN et al. (1956), VOIGHT (1964)
Jurassic	UREY et al. (1951), BOWEN and FRITZ (1963), BOWEN (1966)
Permian	COMPSTON (1960)
Mississippian	LOWENSTAM (1961)
Devonian	COMPSTON (1960)

studies were based on Urey's work during the period 1946–1950, and the ultimate discovery that the ratio of $^{18}O/^{16}O$ in carbonates is controlled by water temperature during formation (EPSTEIN et al., 1951, 1953), although time of formation of the shell, concentration of the isotopes in the water, and shell density often necessitate serious corrections.

The applicability of oxygen isotopic analyses on lacustrine carbonates or fossils for paleotemperature determinations is apparently fraught with difficulties. The relation between the $^{18}O/^{16}O$ ratio and depositional temperature (between $10°$–$40°C$) of fresh-water carbonates is (RANKAMA, 1963):

$$t = 23.9 - 4.8 \, [\delta(O^{18}) - \delta(H_2O)] + 0.14 \, [\delta(O^{18}) - \delta(H_2O)]^2$$

but many ancient lacustrine carbonates were apparently deposited by saline lake waters in environments not too unlike present coastal areas.

The formula for figuring paleotemperature from carbonate deposited under marine or marine-like conditions, as determined by EPSTEIN et al. (1953), is:

$$t = 16.5 - 4.3 \, (^{18}O/^{16}O \text{ sample} - {}^{18}O/^{16}O \text{ sea water}) + 0.14 \, (^{18}O/$$
$$^{16}O \text{ sample} - {}^{18}O/^{16}O \text{ sea water})^2$$

where:

$$^{18}O/^{16}O_{water} = 1000 \left[\frac{^{18}O/^{16}O \text{ sample} - ^{18}O_1{}^{16}O \text{ sea water}}{^{18}O/^{16}O_{\text{sea water}}} \right]$$

although several other equations have been developed (MCCREA, 1950; NAIDIN et al., 1956). From the formulas it is evident that the depositional temperature derived, though a linear function of $\delta^{18}O\%$ (Fig.117), is dependent on the oxygen isotopic composition of the water as well as that of the sample. With marine fossils or samples it may be assumed that environmental water at the time of deposition had the same isotopic composition as present sea water (EPSTEIN and MAYEDA, 1953; LOWENSTAM, 1961), unless circumstances indicate otherwise (LLOYD, 1964). However, in ancient lakes salinity may have been higher or lower than that of sea water, or a rapid evaporation rate (which would also have increased salinity) may have existed, both of which cause concentration of the heavier ^{18}O (LLOYD, 1964), thus paleosalinity of the lacustrine environment must first be determined before accurate paleotemperatures can be determined. This presents untold problems in trying to establish lacustrine paleotemperatures since paleosalinities in most lakes were probably undergoing constant change.

Unfortunately because of the great variability of temperature and salinity in lake basins there is a correspondingly greater range of ^{18}O content than under normal marine conditions. Although the EPSTEIN et al. (1953) equation shows that a change of about 1.0 in the $^{18}O/^{16}O$ ratio of sea water causes an indicated depositional temperature change of little more than 1°C, the slight variation in the present oceans is now known to induce a probable error of about 6 °C (RANKAMA, 1963). Thus, application to lake brines is debatable. Because the $^{18}O/^{16}O$ content of the ocean, as well as that of closed lakes, essentially depends on inflow of fresh water, there may exist a linear relation between the salinity and ^{18}O content of the lake water. Such a linear relation exists (Fig.118) between salinity and ^{18}O content of contaminated sea water (EPSTEIN and MAYEDA, 1953; RANKAMA, 1963), but it is known that sea waters of identical salinity may often have different $\delta^{18}O\%$ contents (BOWEN 1966), a situation which also probably exists in the lacustrine environment.

The $\delta^{18}O$ or $^{18}O/^{16}O$ ratio, like the $\delta^{13}C$ ratio, may be used to distinguish between marine and continental or fresh-water carbonates, the marine environments being enriched in the heavier isotope because of the ^{13}C deficiency caused by CO_2 derived from terrestrial vegetation. Most of the $\delta^{18}O$ analyses of carbonates from West Texas pluvial lake basins fall in between the Quaternary marine range of about -0.2 to 1.9 and the Quaternary freshwater range of about -6 to -10. However, several lacustrine evaporitic carbonates do range from 3.4 to -0.5.

WEBER (1964) believes the wide variations of the $^{18}O/^{16}O$ ratio of fresh water did not exist during interglacial times because the ^{18}O content of meteoric water is altered by glacial ice (EPSTEIN and MAYEDA, 1953), thus carbonates deposited during interglacial times from fresh-water lakes should yield reliable paleotemperatures. WEBER (1964) shows the graph of the ^{18}O content of 157 samples of fresh-water lime-

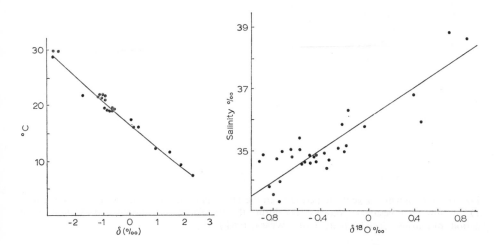

Fig.117. The isotopic temperature scale as devised by EPSTEIN et al. (1953.)

Fig.118. Plot of the salinity of ocean water against ^{18}O content. (After EPSTEIN et al., 1951.)

stones against geologic time, maxima occurring during the Permian–Carboniferous and Quaternary time (Fig.119). Unfortunately the ^{13}C deficiency caused by terrestrial vegetation (KEITH et al., 1964; KEITH and WEBER, 1964), must also be contended with, problems which to date have prevented development of an accurate geothermometer for fresh-water sediments.

The boron method of determining paleosalinities (FREDERICKSON and REY-NOLDS, 1960) seems to hold some future promise but today is beset with problems. Paleosalinity from a boron analysis is figured by:

$$P = B \frac{K_2O_I}{K_2O}$$

where P equals paleosalinity, B is boron in p.p.m., and K_2O_I is percent potassium oxide in illite, the authenticity of the result depending on the illite containing all the boron in the sample (which must be authigenic), the illite being the only potassium mineral present, and the illites from various samples all having the identical K_2Cl content (REYNOLDS, 1965). Paleosalinity determinations, because of these restrictions, may contain significant errors (REYNOLDS, 1965), but application to lacustrine sections may introduce the additional complicating factor of the unknown boron content of ancient lake water.

Mineralogic analyses of certain fossil shells (mainly mollusks) may also be used for paleotemperature and paleosalinity determinations. For instance, the shell of the marine pelecypod *mytilus* shows percentage of aragonite and strontium increasing with temperature, with magnesium content increasing with decreasing salinity: aragonite also increases with decreasing salinity (DODD, 1965, 1966). The applicability to non-marine, lacustrine fossils is not as yet tested.

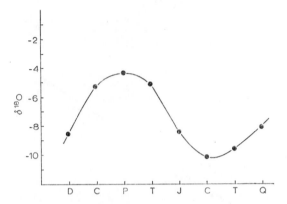

Fig.119. ^{18}O content per geologic period from the Devonian into the Quaternary determined from 157 fresh-water limestones. Notice peaks during the Permian–Carboniferous and Quaternary, all periods of unusual glacial activity. (After WEBER, 1964.)

Geochemical studies of trace elements in modern and ancient clays from both marine and fresh-water environments show that concentrations of B, Cr, Cu, Ga, Ni, and V accurately distinguish depositional environments (POTTER et al., 1963), concentrations being higher in the marine sediments. Whether any of the trace elements other than boron hold any key to either paleosalinity or paleotemperature conditions during deposition is still unknown and thus presents a virgin area for interdisciplinary paleolimnological–geochemical studies.

Chapter 11

SAMPLING METHODS

Most paleolimnological work has and will be done by individual geologists often working without financial support or proper equipment funds, therefore, this discussion of readily available, economical equipment for securing subsurface data. Of course a great deal of shallow work can be expeditiously completed by the long-handled shovel and the post-hole auger: slim-hole hydraulic drilling equipment is generally useless in the upper water-saturated, part of playa fills.

The common post-hole auger, in $1\frac{1}{2}$-inch diameter with standard $\frac{3}{4}$-inch 6-ft. extensions, is unquestionably the cheapest yet best piece of shallow hole drilling equipment available for drilling lacustrine strata (Fig.120). Limitations are shallow depth, time and amount of effort involved, and inability to cut indurated zones. Depth for standard $\frac{3}{4}$-inch steel pipe is about 20 ft. for one man, $\pm$ 40 ft. for two to three men. The one man limit is dictated by length of pipe one man can repeatedly lift (the bit must be cleaned after 4–6 inches of drilling) and lay down for cleaning. The maximum practical depth for the post-hole auger depends principally on time and manpower available, for once a joint is made, time and work necessary to clean the bit become exorbitant. With patience and assistance holes to 40 ft. can be drilled, but depths over about 40 ft. require either light aluminum pipe or an A-frame. Holes over 40 ft. require a second joint for it is difficult to support over about 20 ft. of $\frac{3}{4}$-inch jointed pipe without some type of derrick. Drilling rate for the post-hole auger, which somewhat depends on depth, ranges from about 1 to 6 ft./h in sands and clays. When the sands become very fine-grained and the clays dry and dense, penetration of the auger may, for all practical purposes, cease. Although the post-hole auger will not penetrate indurated lacustrine carbonates or coarse-grained salts it is able to sample very wet, sticky clays. When the clay becomes "mucky" so that the sides of the hole collapse, casing with the new cheap plastic pipe or common gutter downspout may be necessary.

The continuous screw power auger (Fig.121), unlike the post-hole auger, need not be cleaned during drilling since the screw brings samples to the surface. This means an increasing sample contamination and time lag with increasing depth, thus accurate placement of lithologic changes are usually best determined by feel of the bit and later confirmed by the samples. Although having the advantage of a power head, the power auger is difficult to use in clayey lacustrine strata and useless in water-saturated playa sediments, the auger tending to screw into clays like a screw into wood. This can somewhat be prevented by reducing the weight on the drilling bit but this quickly tires the operator. The continuous screw auger is best utilized in sandy lakeside dunes,

maximum depths with a 4.5 H.P. head and a $1\frac{1}{4}$-inch auger being about 30–35 ft.
Depth is restricted by weight of the drill stem and effective sample recovery. With
$1\frac{3}{4}$-inch steel auger, weight for two men becomes prohibitive at about 30–35 ft.
which, fortunately, is just about where sample recovery fails. Sample recovery fails
because of hole enlargement created by increased "whipping" of the drill stem with
increasing depth. Sample recovery also depends somewhat on pitch of the auger, or
distance from crest to crest of the continuous screw on the drill stem. A pitch of about
70–80% (or about 1 inch) of the auger diameter is recommended for most efficient
sample recovery, but slim-hole augers with diameters less than about $2\frac{1}{2}$ inches usually
have a pitch of 150–175%.

The closed spiral auger is best for very dry clays and gravelly clays or small

Fig.120. Using a post-hole auger to depths over about 20 ft. requires a joint. Notice the wooden
"slips" placed on the pipe to prevent dropping into the hole once the pipe is uncoupled. Station wagon
provides a level working platform and a higher reach for the man who supports the long drilling
section while the bit is cleaned. This particular hole, at Mound Lake, Texas, was drilled to 36 ft.
(Photo by the author.)

Fig.121. A continuous screw power auger with detachable power head. (Photo by courtesy of Haynes Manufacturing Company.)

gravels, the open spiral for very loosely consolidated debris. For the very sticky clays the common ship auger is best.

The Hydra-Drill[1] (Fig.122), an economical, hand-operated slim-hole drilling apparatus using carbon steel drill pipe, tungsten carbide tipped drilling tools, and hydraulic pressure, operates efficiently in unconsolidated to semi-consolidated strata to depths of about 200 ft. Hydraulic pressure is provided by a small portable water pump which attaches to a swivel on the ratchet drive. Unfortunately as depth increases sample time lag and contamination increase, thus the Hydra-Drill is good for making holes to a horizon to be cored but useless for detailed subsurface stratigraphic study.

---

[1] Deep Rock Drilling Company, Opelika, Alabama.

Fig.122. The Hydra-Drill undergoing tests. Hydraulic pressure for this test is supplied by the near-by domestic water outlet; however, field conditions utilize a small portable pump and local water. (Photo by Sam Banks, by courtesy of the Deep Rock Drilling Company.)

An obvious second drawback to the Hydra-Drill is the necessity of a water supply.

Several moderately priced slim-hole drilling units which can use a continuous screw auger, a normal drill stem, or a core barrel, are useful for paleolimnological studies. These units, typically rated to use a 3-inch auger to about 50 ft. or to drill and core to 150–200 ft., weigh from 200 to over 1,000 pounds and are therefore impractical for work on soft playas. However, these units are particularly needed when drilling or sampling versitility is required at depths exceeding 30 ft. Water supply is, of course, sometimes a problem.

The most successful corer for lacustrine sediments seems to be the impact type, but with a diameter greater than $\frac{1}{2}$–1 inch: small diameter, slim-hole core barrels generally produce excessive compaction of the core although the split tube soil samplers are fine for unconsolidated lacustrine debris. Fig.123 illustrates one of the most successful impact coring devices used by the author during the last several years. Power is supplied by rotation of the truck's rear wheel which is fitted with an eccentric which alternately pulls the cable sling over the pully which alternately pulls on the wire line running over the masthead and onto which the core barrel is attached. The core barrel itself is a 1–ft. piece of 4-inch pipe with several holes at its upper end which screws onto a 20-ft. piece of 3-inch drill collar that gives weight to the barrel. The 12–18 inch drop caused by alternately pulling the cable pounds the barrel in, the holes at the barrel's upper end releasing water or air pressure allowing easy entrance of the core. The barrel is pulled from the hole by a power winch mounted on the back of the truck, the core extracted from the barrel by the hydraulic press just in front of the truck's rear wheel. Advantages of this type of rig are: (*1*) economy, (*2*) speed of coming in or coming out of the hole, and (*3*) the short, easily managed cores. Disadvantages are: (*1*) the short cores necessitate many round trips, (*2*) the inability of the core barrel to retain water-saturated cores, and (*3*) the inability of the barrel to core hard indurated strata such as salt or carbonates.

Several geophysical methods will provide an indirect "sampling" of subsurface lacustrine sections. Normal seismic methods, unfortunately, are too expensive for individual or even departmental use; however, it is noteworthy that explosion seismology has been successfully used at Searles Lake (MABEY, 1956). Geophysical

Fig.123. Wire-line impact coring unit in operation at Cedar Lake. Notice hydraulic press stand (arrow) used to press core out of barrel. (Photo by the author.)

TABLE XXII

ROCK DENSITIES IN VARIOUS AREAS OF THE WESTERN UNITED STATES

(Modified after CABANISS, 1965)

Area	Pre-Tertiary			Cenozoic			Terrain/ Bouguer
	type rock	maximum	minimum	type rock	maximum	minimum	
South Owens Valley	granites	2.75	2.55	all	2.4	2.0	2.67/2.67
Death Valley	metamorphics	3.09	2.67	—	—	—	2.67/2.67
West Mojave Desert	metamorphics	2.92	2.62	volcanics	2.93	1.44	2.67/2.67
	plutonics	3.02	2.57	sediments	2.58	1.90	—
Indian Wells Valley	plutonics	2.90	2.55	basin sediments	2.3	1.5	—
Nevada Test	sediments and volcanics	2.90	2.50	alluvium	2.2	1.7	—

methods applicable to paleolimnological studies are gravity, magnetics, and shallow seismology.

Singular gravity profiles of several pluvial lake basins in the southwestern United States have been made (CABANISS, 1965), the Bouguer anomalies successfully indicating the bedrock surfaces (Fig.124). Unfortunately gravity results are unduly effected by density variabilities of basin fill, by density contrast between basin fill and basement rock, and particularly by changes in elevation, thus profiles in uncontrolled areas only produce very generalized results. Table XXII illustrates the minimum, maximum, and mean of pre-Tertiary and Cenozoic rock densities from several pluvial lake areas in the southwestern United States, thus giving rough approximations of densities in other like areas. The density of lacustrine basin fill undoubtedly varies from basin to basin because of change in source areas, difference in chemical precipitates, different ground water levels, and difference in relief of source areas. CABANISS (1965) suspects a density of about 2.0 g/cm^3 for the central basin fills and 2.4 g/cm^3 for the near-shore alluvial deposits in the pluvial basins of southwestern United States.

Shallow playa investigations, usually less than 100 ft., can be made by a portable self-powered seismic timer which measures the travel-time of an artifically induced seismic shock wave. The travel-time of the microseismic shock waves depends mainly on density of the rock layers, thus velocities through lacustrine fills are generally slow, but become increasingly faster with depth. Uppermost playa "mucks" generally have a velocity of 500–1,000 ft./sec, sandy layers increasing to about 3,000 ft./sec; however, for any one lithology a wide velocity range may exist due to porosity changes, contaminants such as clays and/or gravels, and variable cementing agents. The shallow modern fills in the West Texas pluvial lake basins generally have velocities

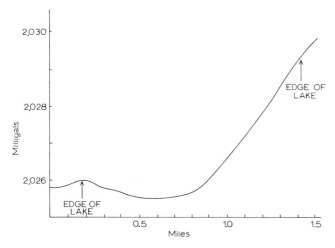

Fig.124. The simple Bouguer Anomaly across North Alkali Flat playa, a remnant of a Pleistocene lake in the Lordsburg, New Mexico, area. A density of 2.0 g/cm^3 was assumed for surface sediments. (Modified after CABANISS, 1965.)

of about 750–950 ft./sec, older dense, compacted lacustrine clays about 8,000–10,000 ft./sec.

A microseismic survey can be conducted by two persons, one operating the seismic timer and one supplying the energy. By graphing distance of shock origin (generally supplied by hitting a steel plate with a sledge hammer) to recorded velocity in milleseconds, the depth to different lacustrine layers can be computed by the formula:

$$D = \frac{D_E}{2} \sqrt{\frac{V_2 - V_1}{V_2 + V_1}}$$

where D equals depth to the discontinuity, D_E refers to distance of energy from timer, V_1 is the velocity of the upper layer and V_2 the velocity of the lower faster zone. Velocity in ft./sec is given by dividing D_E by recorded time in msec and multiplying by 1,000 msec/sec. Unfortunately such seismic studies give reasonable results only if the lacustrine layers continually increase in density (velocity) with depth. If a very hard, lacustrine carbonate layer is interbedded with softer lacustrine clays the critical depths below the hard layer cannot be calculated.

Ancient lake basins that today partly contain water, such as Bonneville, may be studied by the high resolution marine sonoprobe or an electrosonic profiler (Geotech, Dallas, Texas). The sonoprobe is accurate to about 300 ft, the profiler to about 3,000 ft.; however, the author is unaware of any completed lacustrine studies utilizing these instruments.

Submarine topography can be studied by using a fathometer, a continuous recording unit being most applicable (SCHOLL and STUIVER, 1967). Penetration of the subsurface requires a high signal volume and lower frequencies (J. J. Dowling, personal communication, 1967), but resolution is not as good as with the electrosonic profiler. An echo sounder was used in Lake Corangamite, Australia in 1964, sub-bottom profiles[1] between the lacustrine fill and bedrock being easily discernible in many places.

---

[1] Profiles by courtesy of D. T. Currey, Senior Geologist, State Rivers and Water Supply, Armadale, Australia.

Chapter 12

FUTURE PALEOLIMNOLOGICAL APPLICATIONS

The most important application of paleolimnological study has been in the field of paleoclimatology. As documented throughout this book there is a voluminous amount of data concerning Pleistocene climatic parameters in the Northern Hemisphere but, other than the Australian studies, a general paucity of data from the Southern Hemisphere. Research shows contemporaneous climatic changes between Europe and North America during Tahoka time (22,000–14,000 years B.P.) and pollen evidence and deep-sea cores indicate like changes between North America, South America, and Australia. Therefore, perhaps the greatest future contribution of paleolimnology will be resolution of chronology of paleoclimatic parameters, as well as determination of the parameters themselves.

Development of water resources in semi-arid to arid lands is best implemented by first investigating, geomorphologically and structurally, the natural basins. As we find in many areas of the western United States and Mexico, basins which once held paleolakes interfere with local aquifers and often allow saline water to enter aquifers. Presence of a saliferous lacustrine section is not conducive to development of potable water supplies; however, lacustrine sands and gravels, mainly in the high ends of the basins, or fluviatile clastics around basin margins, often contain potable water. Many intermontane basins, perhaps with or without present or Late Pleistocene saliferous playas, have a thick Upper Pleistocene fluviatile fill over an even thicker lacustrine section of unknown age. For instance, in the Hueco bolson, near El Paso, Texas, a deep water well test revealed about 1,050 ft. of fluviatile sands and gravels over at least 3,313 ft. of lacustrine sand, silt, and clay[1] (T. E. Cliett, personal communication, 1967). Under such conditions fresh water is usually confined to the fluviatile section, saline water to the near-surface and deeper lacustrine sections except that pressure from the compacting, buried lacustrine section will often force saline water into the overlying gravels. Thus, a knowledge and recognition of ancient lacustrine sediments is invaluable for such hydrologic studies.

The increasing demands imposed on the world's natural resources focus attention on the many commercial salts frequently found in lacustrine sections. Removal of these salts, some necessary to farming, some to basic industry, provides additional income to both country and local inhabitants. Locations of probable commercial lacustrine salt occurrences are best determined and profitably exploited by an inter-disciplinary team of paleolimnologists—geochemists and engineers.

---

[1]Bedrock now thought to be about 7,000 ft. below ground surface.

As previously suggested (p.131) critical examination of aerial photographs of various celestial objects, for evidence of erosive or depositional features produced by water, is an important aspect of our space program; the Jet Propulsion Laboratory, California, is now searching for nivial features on Mars (F. A. Wade, personal communication, 1967). Obviously presence of erosional features produced by water would be invaluable in establishing environmental parameters, past or present.

The Geotechnics Branch, Terrestrial Sciences Laboratory, Air Force Cambridge Research Laboratories, Bedford, Massachusetts, has been investigating the geomorphology, structure, and hydrology of desert playas as possible emergency landing fields for aircraft or space capsules. Such studies also apply to celestial objects for it could be disastrous to land a manned or unmanned capsule in the middle of either a water-saturated playa or in a playa criss-crossed by deep, wide desiccation features.

Other possibilities come to mind, but these few examples adequately illustrate that the future of paleolimnological study is wide indeed.

REFERENCES

AHLMANN, H. W., 1924. Le niveau de glaciation comme fonction de l'accumulation d'humidité sous forme solide. *Géograph. Ann.*, 6: 223–272.

ALBRITTON JR., C. C. and BRYAN, K., 1939. Quaternary stratigraphy in the Davis Mountains, Trans-Pecos, Texas. *Bull. Geol. Soc. Am.*, 50: 1423–1474.

ALLEN, D. and CHEATUM, E. P., 1961. A Pleistocene molluscan fauna near Byers, Clay County, Texas. *J. Graduata, Res. Center*, 29: 137–169.

AMBROGGI, R. P., 1966. Water under the Sahara. *Sci. Am.*, 214: 21–29.

ANDERSON, E. R., 1954. Water-loss investigations: Lake Hefner studies, Technical report. *U.S., Geol. Surv., Profess. Papers*, 269: 157 pp.

ANDERSON, S. T., 1961. Vegetation and its environment in Denmark in the Early Weichselian Glacial. *Denmarks Geol. Undersoegelse*, II, 75.

ANTEVS, E., 1925. Retreat of the last ice sheet in eastern Canada. *Can., Geol. Surv., Mem.*, 146: 142 pp.

ANTEVS, E., 1928. The last glaciation. *Am. Geograph. Soc.*, 17: 292 pp.

ANTEVS, E., 1935. Age of the Clovis Lake clays. *Phil. Acad. Natl. Sci. Proc.*, 87: 304–312.

ANTEVS, E., 1938. Post pluvial climatic variations in the southwest. *Am. Meteorol. Soc.*, 19: 190–93.

ANTEVS, E., 1948. Climatic changes and pre-white man. *Univ. Utah Bull.*, 38: 168–191.

ANTEVS, E., 1952. Cenozoic climates of the Great Basin. *Geol. Res.*, 40: 94–108.

ANTEVS, E., 1953. Geochronology of the Deglacial and Neothermal ages. *J. Geol.*, 61: 195–230.

ANTEVS, E., 1954. Climate of New Mexico during the last glacial-pluvial. *J. Geol.*, 62: 182–191.

ANTEVS, E., 1957. Geological tests of the varve and radiocarbon chronologies. *J. Geol.*, 65: 129–148.

ANTEVS, E., 1959. Geologic age of the Lehner Mammoth site. *Am. Antiquity*, 25: 31–34.

ARNOLD, J. R. and LIBBY, W. F., 1951. Age determinations by radiocarbon content: check with samples of known age. *Science*, 110: 678–680.

ATTREE, R. W., CABELL, M. J., CUSHING, R. L. and PIERON, J. J.,1962. A calorimetric determination of the half-life of ^{230}Th and consequent revision of its neutron capture cross-section. *Can. J. Phys.*, 40: 194–201.

BAILEY, R. W., 1941. Climate and settlement of the arid region. *Climate and Man-Agr. Yearbook*, 192: 188–196.

BAKER, F. C., 1920. The life of the Pleistocene or glacial period as recorded in the deposits laid down by the great ice sheets. *Univ. Ill Bull*, 17: 476 pp.

BAKER, F. S., 1944. Mountain climates of the western United States. *Ecol., Monographs*, 14: 229–243.

BARBOUR, E. H. and SCHULTZ, C. B., 1934. A new giant camel, *Titanotylopus Nebraskensis, Nov. Univ. Nebr. State, Bull.*, 1: 291–294.

BARNES, J. W., LANG, E. J. and POTRATZ, H. A., 1956. Ratio of ionium to uranium in coral limestone. *Science*, 124: 175–176.

BEADNELL, H. G. L., 1909. *An Egyptian Oasis*. Murray, London, 248 pp.

BELL, B., 1953. Solar variations as an explanation of climate change. In: H. SHAPLEY (Editor), *Climatic Change, Evidence, Causes, and Effects*. Harvard Univ. Press, Cambridge, Mass., pp.123–136.

BENT, A. M., 1960. *Pollen Analysis at Deadman Lake, Chuska Mountains, New Mexico*. Thesis, Univ. Minnesota, Minneapolis, Minn. 22 pp.

BENT, A. M. and WRIGHT JR., H. E., 1963. Pollen analysis of surface materials and lake sediments from the Chuska Mountains, New Mexico. *Bull. Geol. Soc. Am.*, 74: 491–500.

BERRY, E. W., 1916. The Lower Eocene floras of southeastern North America. *U.S., Geol. Surv., Profess. Papers*, 91: 481 pp.

BLANCKENHORN, M., 1912. *Naturwissenschaftliche Studien am Toten Meer und am Jordantal.* Friedländer, Berlin, 478 S.

BLANCKENHORN, M., 1921–1922. Die Steinzeit Palästina-Syriens und Nordafrikas. In: *Das Land der Bibel.* Friedländer, Leipzig, 3: 49 pp.; 4:46 pp.

BLANEY, H. F., 1957. Evaporation study at Silver Lake in the Mojave Desert. *Trans. Am. Geophys. Union,* 38: 209–215.

BLOCH, M. R., 1965. A hypothesis for the change of ocean levels depending on the albedo of the polar ice caps. *Palaeogeography, Palaeoclimatol., Palaeoecol.,* 1: 127–142.

BOBEK, H., 1937. Die Rolle der Eiszeit in Nordwestiran: *Z. Gletscherk.,* 25: 130–183.

BOBEK, H., 1941. Die gegenwärtige u. eiszeitliche Vergletscherung im Zentralkurdischen Hochgebirge. *Z. Gletscherk.,* 27: 50–87.

BOBEK, H., 1964. Nature and implications of Quaternary climatic changes in Iran. *Arid Zone Res.,* 20: 403–413.

BONYTHON, C. W., 1955. The evaporation rate III. In: *Lake Eyre, South Australia, The Great Flooding of 1949–1950.* Roy. Geograph. Soc. Australasia, S. Australia Branch, Adelaide, pp.37–57.

BONYTHON, C. W., 1956. The salt of Lake Eyre—its occurrence in Madigan Gulf and its possible origin. *Trans. Roy. Soc. Australia,* 79: 66–92.

BONYTHON, C. W., 1958. Lake Eyre. In: R. J. BEST (Editor), *Introducing South Australia.* Australia New Zealand Assoc. Advan. Sci., Adelaide, pp.127–128.

BONYTHON, C. W., 1960. A decade of watching for water in Lake Eyre. *Proc. Roy. Geograph. Soc. Australasia, S. Australia Branch,* 61: 1–8.

BONYTHON, C. W., 1961. The accurate determination of the levels of Lake Eyre. *Proc. Roy. Geograph. Soc. Australasia, S. Australia Branch,* 62: 57–63.

BONYTHON, C. W., 1963. Further light on river floods reaching Lake Eyre. *Proc. Roy. Geog. Soc. Australasia, S. Australia Branch,* 64: 9–22.

BONYTHON, C. W. and MASON, B., 1953. The filling and drying of Lake Eyre. *Geograph J.* 119: 321–330.

BOWEN, R., 1961a. Paleotemperature analyses of Mesozoic Belemnoidea from Germany and Poland. *J. Geol.,* 69: 75–83.

BOWEN, R., 1961b. Paleotemperature analyses of Mesozoic Belemnoidea from Australia and New Guinea. *Bull. Geol. Soc. Am.,* 72: 769–774.

BOWEN, R., 1961c. Paleotemperature analyses of Belemnoidea and Jurassic paleoclimatology. *J. Geol.,* 69: 309–320.

BOWEN, R., 1961d. Oxygen isotope paleotemperature analyses of Mesozoic Belemnoidea from Europe, India, Japan. *J. Paleontol.,* 35: 1077–1084.

BOWEN, R., 1963. Oxygen isotope paleotemperature measurements on Lower Jurassic Belemnoidea from Bamberg (Bavaria) Germany. *Experientia* 19: 401–403.

BOWEN, R., 1966. *Paleotemperature Analysis.* Elsevier, Amsterdam, 265 pp.

BOWEN, R. and FONTES, J. C., 1963. Paleotemperatures indiquées par l'analyse isotopique de fossiles du Cretace inférieur des Hautes Alpes (France). *Experientia,* 19: 268–275.

BOWEN, R. and FRITZ, P., 1963. Oxygen isotope paleotemperature analyses of Lower and Middle Jurassic fossils from Pliensbach, Württemberg, Germany. *Experientia,* 19: 461–470.

BOWLER, J. M. and HARFORD, L. B., 1966. Quaternary tectonics and the evolution of the Riverine Plain near Echuca, Victoria. *J. Geol. Soc. Australia,* 13: 339–354.

BRADLEY, W. H., 1928. Algae reef and oölites of the Green River Formation. *U.S., Geol., Surv., Profess. Papers,* 154: 203–233.

BRADLEY, W. H., 1963. Paleolimnology. In: D. G. FREY (Editor), *Limnology in North America.* Univ. Wisc. Press, Madison, Wisc., pp.621–652.

BROECKER, W. S., 1961. Radiocarbon dating of Late Quaternary deposits, south Louisiana: a discussion. *Bull. Geol. Soc. Am.,* 72: 159–162.

BROECKER, W. S., 1965. Isotope geochemistry and the Pleistocene climatic record. In: H. E. WRIGHT, JR. and D. G. FREY (Editors), *Quaternary of the United States.* Princeton Univ. Press, Princeton, N.J., pp.737–753.

BROECKER, W. S., 1966. Absolute dating and the astronomical theory of glaciation. *Science,* 151: 299–304.

BROECKER, W. S. and KAUFMAN, A., 1965. Radiocarbon chronology of Lake Lahontan and Lake Bonneville, 2. *Bull. Geol. Soc. Am.,* 76: 537–566.

BROECKER, W. S. and KULP, J. L., 1956. The radiocarbon method of age determination. *Am. Antiquity*, 22: 1–11.

BROECKER, W. S. and ORR, P. C., 1958. Radiocarbon chronology of Lake Lahontan and Lake Bonneville. *Bull. Geol. Soc. Am.*, 69: 1009–1032.

BROECKER, W. S. and WALTON, A., 1959a. The geochemistry of ^{14}C in fresh-water systems. *Geochim. Cosmochim. Acta*, 16: 15–38.

BROECKER, W. S. and WALTON, A., 1959b. Re-evaluation of the salt chronology of several great basin lakes. *Bull. Geol. Soc. Am.*, 70: 601–618.

BROECKER W. S., EWING, M. and HEEZEN, B. C., 1960. Evidence for an abrupt change in climate close to 11,000 years ago. *Am. J. Sci.*, 258: 429–448.

BROOKS, C. E. P., 1949a. *Climate Through the Ages*. McGraw-Hill, New York, N.Y., 395 pp.

BROOKS, C. E. P., 1949b. Post-glacial climatic changes in the light of recent glaciological research. *Geograph. Ann.*, 31.

BROUWER, D., 1953. The polar motion and changes in the earth's orbit. In: H. SHAPLEY (Editor), *Climatic Change, Evidence, Causes, and Effects*. Harvard Univ. Press, Cambridge, Mass., pp.159–164.

BROUWER, D. and VAN WOERKOM, A. J., 1950. The secular variations of the orbital elements of the principal planets. *Astron. Papers*, 13: 81.

BROWNE, W. R., 1945. An attempted post-Tertiary chronology for Australia. *Limnol. Soc., New S. Wales, Proc.*, 70: 5–24.

BRÜCKNER, E., 1890. Die Klimaschwankungen seit 1700. *Geograf. Abhandl.*, 4: 325 S.

BRYAN, K., 1941. Correlation of the deposits of Sandia Cave, New Mexico, with the glacial chronology. *Smithsonian Inst., Misc. Collections*, 99: 69.

BRYAN, K., 1950. Geologic interpretation of the deposits. In: E. W. HAURY (Editor), *The Stratigraphy and Archaeology of Ventana Cave, Arizona*. Univ. New Mexico Press, Albuquerque, N.M., pp.75–126.

BÜDEL, J., 1949. Die räumliche und zeitliche Gliederung des Eiszeitklimas. *Naturwissenschaften*, 36: 105–139.

BUTZER, K. W., 1964. *Environment and Archeology*. Aldine Publ. Co., Chicago, Ill., 524 pp.

CABANISS, G. H., 1965. Geophysical studies of playa basins. In: J. T. NEAL (Editor), *Geology, Mineralogy, and Hydrology of U.S. Playas—Air Force Cambridge Res. Lab. Environ. Res. Paper*, 96: 123–147.

CALDER, K. L., 1949. Eddy diffusion and evaporation in flow over aerodynamically smooth and rough surfaces. *Quart. J. Mech. Appl. Math.*, 2: 153–176.

CARLSTON, C. W., 1963. Free and incised meanders in the United States and their geomorphic and paleoclimatic implications. *Geol. Soc. Am., Spec. Paper*, 76: 28–29 (abstract).

CARRUTHERS, D., 1914. *Unknown Mongolia*. Hutchinson and Co., London, 650 pp.

CARTER, G. F., 1956. On soil color and time. *Southern J. Anthropol.*, 12: 295–324.

CATON-THOMPSON, G. and GARDNER, E. W., 1929. Recent work on the problem of Lake Moeris. *Geograph. J.*, 73: 20–60.

CATON-THOMPSON, G. and GARDNER, E. W., 1932. The prehistoric geography of Kharga Oasis. *Geograph. J.*, 80: 369–409.

CATON-THOMPSON, G. and GARDNER, E. W., 1934. *The Desert Fayum*. Roy. Anthropol. Soc., London, 167 pp.

CAYTON, R. N. and DEGENS, E. T., 1959. Use of carbon isotope analyses of carbonates for differentiating freshwater and marine sediments. *Bull. Am. Assoc. Petrol. Geologists*, 43: 890–897.

CHAMBERLIN, T. C., 1899. An attempt to frame a working hypothesis of the cause of glacial periods on an atmospheric basis. *J. Geol.*, 7: 545–584.

CHANEY, R. W., 1963. Some observations on climatic relations of Tertiary floras bordering the North Pacific basin. In: A. E. M. NAIRN (Editor), *Problems in Paleoclimatology*. Interscience, London, pp.40–43.

CHARLESWORTH, J. K., 1957. *The Quaternary Era*. Edward Arnold, Ltd., London, 1700 pp.

CHEATUM, E. P. and ALLEN, D., 1963. An ecological comparison of the Ben Franklin and Clear Creek local molluscan faunas in Texas. *J. Graduate Res. Center*, 31: 174–179.

CHEATUM, E. P. and ALLEN, D., 1965. Pleistocene land and freshwater mollusks from North Texas. *Sterkiana*, 18: 1–16.

CHEATUM, E. P., ALLEN, D. and SLAUGHTER, B. H., 1966. Notes on the alluvial history of the Lampasas River, Texas. *J. Graduate Res. Center*, 35: 48–54.

CHEMEKOV, Y., 1960. *Dokl., Earth. Sci. Sect.* (*English Transl.*), 127 (1960): 675.

CLARKE, R., 1960. *East Anglia*. Thames and Hudson, London, 240 pp.

CLISBY, K. H. and SEARS, P. B., 1956. San Augustin plains–Pleistocene climatic changes. *Science*, 124: 537–539.

COLEMAN, A. P., 1941. *The Last Million Years. A History of the Pleistocene in North America*. Univ. Toronto Press, Toronto, 216 pp.

COLINVAUX, P. A., 1964. Origin of ice ages: pollen evidence from Arctic Alaska. *Science*, 145: 707–708.

COMPSTON, W., 1960. The carbon isotopic composition of certain marine invertebrates and coals from the Australian Permian. *Geochim. Cosmochim. Acta*, 18: 1–22.

COPE, E. D., 1892. A hyaena and other carnivora from Texas. *Proc. Acad. Nat. Sci., Philadelphia*, 44: 326–327.

CORNISH, V., 1897. On the formation of sand dunes. *Geograph. J.*, 9: 278–309.

CRAIG, H., 1954. Carbon ^{13} in plants and the relationships between C^{13} and C^{14} variations in nature. *J. Geol.*, 62: 115–149.

CRATHORN, A. R., 1953. Use of an acetylene-filled counter for natural radiocarbon. *Nature*, 172: 632.

CRITTENDEN, M. D., JR., 1963. New data on the isostatic deformation of Lake Bonneville. *U.S. Geol. Surv., Profess. Papers*, 454-E: 31 pp.

CROLL, J., 1875. *Climate and Time in their Geological Relations: A Theory of Secular Changes of the Earth's Climate*. Stanford, London, 577 pp.

CURRAY, J. R., 1960. Sediments and history of Holocene transgression, continental shelf, northwest Gulf of Mexico. In: F. P. SHEPARD, F. B. PHLEGER and TJ. H. VAN ANDEL (Editors), *Recent Sediments, Northwest Gulf of Mexico*, Am. Assoc. Petrol. Geologists, Tulsa, Okla., 221–226.

CURRAY, J. R., 1961. Late Quaternary sea-level-a discussion. *Bull. Geol. Soc., Am.*, 72: 1707–1712.

CURRAY, J. R., 1965. Late Quaternary history, continental shelves of the United States. In: H. E. WRIGHT JR. and D. G. FREY (Editors), *Quaternary of the United States*. Princeton Univ. Press, Princeton, N.J., pp.723–735.

DALQUEST, W. W., 1962. The Good Creek Formation, Pleistocene of Texas, and its fauna. *J. Paleontol.*, 36: 568–582.

DAMON, P. E., LONG, A. and GREY, D. C., 1965. Fluctuations of atmospheric C^{14} during the last six millennia. *Proc., 6th Intern. Conf. Radiocarbon Tritium Dating-Div. Tech. Inform. At. Energy Comm. Conf.* 650652: 415–421.

DANA, J. D., 1856. On American geological history. *Am. J. Sci.*, 22: 305–334.

DAVID, T. W. E., 1932. *Explanatory Notes to Accompany a New Geological Map of the Commonwealth of Australia*. Australian Medical Publ. Co., Sydney, N.S.W., 177 pp.

DAVID, T. W. E., 1950. *The Geology of the Commonwealth of Australia*. Edward Arnold, London, 1: 747 pp.; 2: 618 pp.

DAVIS, J., 1946. The peat deposits of Florida, their occurrence, development, and uses. *Florida, Geol. Surv., Geol., Bull.*, 30: 247 pp.

DEEVEY, E. S., 1944. Pollen analysis and Mexican archaeology: an attempt to apply the method. *Am. Antiquity*, 10: 135–149.

DEEVEY, JR., E. S., 1958. Bogs. *Scientific Am.*, 199. 4: 114–122.

DEEVEY JR., E. S., GROSS, M. S., HUTCHINSON, G. E. and KAYBILL, H. L., 1954. The natural C^{14} control of materials from hard-water lakes. *Proc. Natl. Acad. Sci , U.S.*, 40: 255–288.

DE GEER, G., 1912. A geochronology of the last 12,000 years. *Compt. Rend., Intern. Géol. Conf., 11e, Stockholm, 1910*, 1: 241–258.

DE GEER, G., 1940. Geochronologia suecica principles. *Kgl. Svenska Vetenskapsakad. Handl.*, 18: 367 pp.

DESNOYERS, J., 1829. Observations sur un ensemble de dépôts marins plus récents que les terrains Tertiares du bassin de la Seine, et constituant une formation géologique distincte: precedées d'un apercu de la non-simultanéité des bassins Tertiaires. *Ann. Sci. Nat., Paris*, 16: 171–491.

DEVRIES, H. P., 1959. Measurement and use of natural radiocarbon. In: P. H. ABELSON (Editor), *Researches in Geochemistry*. Wiley, New York, N.Y., 169–189.

DILLON, L. S., 1956. Wisconsin climate and life zones in North America. *Science*, 123: 167–176.

DODD, J. R., 1965. Environmental control of strontium and magnesium in *Mytilus*. *Geochim. Cosmochim. Acta*, 29: 385–398.

DODD, J. R., 1966. Diagenetic stability of temperature-sensitive skeletal properties in *Mytilus* from the Pleistocene of California. *Bull. Geol. Soc. Am.*, 77: 1213–1224.

DOELL, R. R. and COX, A., 1961. Paleomagnetism. *Advan. Geophys.*, 8: 221–313.

DONN, W. L. and EWING, M., 1966. A theory of Ice Ages III. *Science*, 152: 1706–1712.

DONN, W. L., FARRAND, W. R. and EWING, M., 1962. Pleistocene ice volumes and sea-level lowering. *J. Geol.*, 70: 206–214.

DORF, E., 1955. Plants and the geologic time scale. *Geol. Soc. Am.*, *Spec. Paper*, 62: 575–592.

DOUGLASS, A. E., 1919, 1936. Climatic cycles and tree growth. *Carnegie Inst. Wash. Publ.*, 289 (2): 166 pp.; (3): 171 pp.

DIETHORN, W., 1956. Thesis, Carnegie Inst. Technol., Wash., D.C., (unpublished).

DUBOIS, E., 1895. *The Climates of the Geological Past and their Relation to the Evolution of the Sun*. Sonneschein, London, 167 pp.

DUNBAR, C. O., 1960. *Historical Geology*. Wiley, New York, N.Y., 500 pp.

DUNN, J. R., 1953. The origin of deposits of tufa in Mono Lake. *J. Sediment. Petrol.*, 23: 18–23.

DUREGNE, M. E., 1904. La grande montagne de la Teste de Buch: *Ann. Club Alpin Franç.*, 30: 388–415.

DURHAM, J. W., 1950. Cenozoic marine climates of the Pacific Coast. *Bull. Geol. Soc. Am.*, 61: 1243–1264.

DURHAM, J. W., JOHNS, R. H. and SAVAGE, D. E., 1954. Marine-nonmarine relationships in the Cenozoic sections of California. *Calif. ,Div. Mines Bull.*, 170: 59–71.

EARDLEY, A. J. and GVOSDETSKY, V., 1960. Analysis of Pleistocene core from Great Salt Lake, Utah. *Bull. Geol. Soc. Am.*, 71: 1323–1344.

EMERY, K., 1958. Shallow submerged marine terraces of southern California. *Bull. Geol. Soc. Am.*, 69: 39–60.

EMILIANI, C., 1954a. Depth habits of some species of pelagic Foraminifera as indicated by oxygen isotope ratios. *Am. J. Sci.*, 252: 149–158.

EMILIANI, C., 1954b. Temperatures of Pacific bottom waters and polar superficial waters during the Tertiary. *Science*, 119: 853–855.

EMILIANI, C., 1955a. Pleistocene temperature variations in the Mediterranean. *Quaternaria*, 2: 87–98.

EMILIANI, C., 1955b. Pleistocene temperature. *J. Geol.*, 63: 538–578.

EMILIANI, C., 1956. Oligocene and Miocene temperatures of the equatorial and subtropical Atlantic Ocean. *J. Geol.*, 64: 281–288.

EMILIANI, C., 1958. Paleotemperature analysis of core 280 and Pleistocene correlations. *J. Geol.*, 66: 264–275.

EMILIANI, C., 1961. The temperature decrease of surface sea-water in high latitudes and of abyssal-hadal water in open oceanic basins during the past 75 million years. *Deep-Sea Res.*, 8: 144–147.

EMILIANI, C., 1964. Paleotemperature analysis of the Caribbean cores A254-BR-C and CP-28. *Bull. Geol. Soc. Am.*, 75: 129–144.

EMILIANI, C. and EDWARDS, G., 1953. Tertiary ocean bottom temperatures. *Nature*, 171: 887–889.

EMILIANI, C. and GEISS, J., 1959. On glaciations and their causes. *Geol. Rundschau*, 46: 576–601.

EPSTEIN, S. and LOWENSTAM, H. A., 1953. Temperature-shell growth relations of Recent and interglacial Pleistocene shoal-water biota from Bermuda. *J. Geol.*, 61: 424–438.

EPSTEIN, S. and MAYEDA, T. R., 1953. Variation in O^{18} content of waters from natural sources. *Geochim. Cosmochim. Acta.*, 5: 213–244.

EPSTEIN, S., BUCHSBAUM, R., LOWENSTAM, H. and UREY, H. C., 1951. Carbonate-water isotopic temperature scale. *Bull. Geol. Soc. Am.*, 62: 417–442.

EPSTEIN, S., BUCHSBAUM, R., LOWENSTAM, H. and UREY, H. C., 1953. Revised carbonate-water isotopic temperature scale. *Bull. Geol. Soc. Am.*, 64: 1315–1326.

ERICSON, D. B., 1961. Pleistocene climatic record in some deep-sea sediment cores. *Ann. New York Acad. Sci.*, 95: 537–541.

ERICSON, D. B. and WOLLIN, G., 1964. *The Deep and the Past*. Knopf, New York, N.Y.

ERICSON, D. B., BROECKER, W. S., KULP, J. L. and WOLLIN, G., 1956. Late-Pleistocene climates and deep-sea sediments. *Science*, 124: 385–389.

ERICSON, D. B., EWING, M., WOLLIN, G. and HEEZEN, B. C., 1961. Atlantic deep-sea sediment cores. *Bull. Geol. Soc. Am.*, 72: 193–286.

ERICSON, D. B., EWING, M. and WOLLIN, G., 1963. Plio-Pleistocene boundary in deep-sea sediments. *Science*, 139: 727.

ERICSON, D. B., EWING, M. and WOLLIN, G., 1964. The Pleistocene epoch in deep-sea sediments. *Science*, 146: 723–732.

EVERNDEN, J. G., SAVAGE, D. E., CURTIS, G. H. and JAMES, G. T., 1964. Potassium-argon dates and the Cenozoic mammalian chronology of North America. *Am. J. Sci.*, 262: 145–198.

EWING, M. and DONN, W. L., 1956. A theory of Ice Ages. *Science*, 123: 1061–1066.

EWING, M. and DONN, W. L., 1958. A theory of Ice Ages, 2. *Science*, 127: 1159–1162.

EWING, M. and DONN, W. L., 1961. Pleistocene climate changes. *Proc., Ist., Intern. Congr. Arctic Geol.* Univ. Toronto Press, Toronto, Ont.

FAIRBRIDGE, R. W., 1948. Notes on the geomorphology of the Pelsart group of the Houtman's Abrolhos Islands. *J. Roy. Soc. West Australia*, 33: 1–43.

FAIRBRIDGE, R. W., 1961a. African Ice-age aridity. in: A. E. M. NAIRN (Editor), *Problems in Palaeoclimatology*. Interscience, London, pp.356–360.

FAIRBRIDGE, R. W., 1961b. Eustatic changes in sea level. In: L. H. AHERNS, F. PRESS, K. RANKAMA and S. K. RUNKORN (Editors), *Physics and Chemistry of the Earth*. Pergamon Press, New York, N.Y., 4: 99–185.

FAIRBRIDGE, R. W., 1961c. Convergence of evidence on climatic change and ice ages. *Ann. New York Acad. Sci.*, 95: 542–579.

FAIRBRIDGE, R. W., 1964. African Ice-age aridity. In: A. E. M. NAIRN (Editor), *Problems in Palaeoclimatology*. Interscience, London, pp.356–360.

FAKEY, J. J., 1962. Saline minerals of the Green River Formation. *U.S., Geol. Surv., Profess.Papers*, 405: 50 pp.

FANALE, F. P. and SCHAEFFER, O. A., 1965. Helium-uranium ratios for Pleistocene and Tertiary fossil aragonites. *Science*, 149: 312–316.

FEDOROVICH, B., 1940. Some fundamental considerations concerning the origin and development of the arid relief. *Acad. Sci. U.S.S.R., Ser. Geograph. Geophys.*, 6: 885–910.

FERGUSSON, G. L., 1955. Radiocarbon dating system. *Nucleonics*, 13: 18–23.

FETH, J. H., 1959. Re-evaluation of the salt chronology of several great basins lake: a discussion. *Bull. Geol. Soc. Am.*, 70: 637–640.

FETH, J. H., 1964. Review and annotated bibliography of ancient lake deposits (Precambrian to Pleistocene) in the western United States. *U.S., Geol. Surv., Bull.*, 1080: 119 pp.

FISK, H. and MCFARLAN, E., 1955. Late Quaternary deltaic deposits of the Mississippi River. *Geol. Soc. Am., Spec. Paper*, 62: 279–302.

FJERDINGSTAD, E., 1954. The subfossil algae flora of the Lake Bolling So and its limnological interpretation. *Kgl. Danske Videnskab. Selskab, Biol. Skrifter*, 7 (6): 1–56.

FLINT, R. F., 1937. Pleistocene drift border in eastern Washington. *Bull. Geol. Soc. Am.*, 48: 203–231.

FLINT, R. F., 1947. *Glacial Geology and the Pleistocene Epoch*. Wiley, New York, N.Y., 589 pp.

FLINT, R. F., 1955. Rates of advance and retreat of the margin of the Late Wisconsin ice sheet. *Am. J. Sci.*, 253: 249–255.

FLINT, R. F., 1957. *Glacial and Pleistocene Geology*. Wiley, New York, N.Y., 553 pp.

FLINT, R. F. and DEEVEY, E. S., 1951. Radiocarbon dating of Late Pleistocene events. *Am. J. Sci.*, 249: 257–300.

FLOHN, H., 1952. Zur Aerologie der Polargebiete. *Meteorol. Rundschau*, 5: 81–87.

FLOHN, H., 1953. Studien über die atmosphärische Zirkulation in der letzten Eiszeit. *Erdkunde*, 7: 266–275.

FORBES, E., 1846. On the connection between the distribution of the existing fauna and flora of the British Isles, and the geological change which has affected their area, especially during the epoch of the Northern Drift. *Gt. Britain, Geol. Surv., Mem.*, 1: 336–432.

FOREMAN, F., 1955. Palynology in southern North America, II. A study of two cores from lake sediments of the Mexico City basin. *Bull. Geol. Soc. Am.*, 66: 475–510.

FREDERICKSON, A. F. and REYNOLDS, R. C., 1960. Geochemical method for determining paleosalinity. *Clays Clay Minerals, Proc. Natl. Conf. Clays Clay Minerals*, 8: 203–213.

FRENZEL B. and TROLL, C., 1952. Die vegetationszonen des nördlichen Eurasiens während der letzten Eiszeit. *Eiszeitalter Gegenwart* 2: 154–167.

FREY, D. G., 1953. Regional aspects of the late-glacial and post-glacial pollen succession of southeastern North Carolina, *Ecol. Monographs*, 23: 289–313.

FRIEDMAN, G. M., 1962. On sorting, sorting coefficients, and the lognormality of the grain-size distribution of sandstones. *J. Geol.*, 70: 737–753.

FRYE, J. C. and LEONARD, A. B., 1952. Pleistocene geology of Kansas. *Kansas, Geol. Surv., Bull.* 99: 230 pp.

FRYE, J. C. and LEONARD, A. B., 1957a. Studies of Cenozoic geology along eastern margin of Texas High Plains, Armstrong to Howard Counties. *Univ. Texas, Dept. Invest.*, 32: 62 pp.

FRYE, J. C. and LEONARD, A. B., 1957b, Ecological interpretations of Pliocene and Pleistocene stratigraphy in the Great Plains region. *Am. J. Sci.*, 255: 1–11.

FRYE, J. C. and LEONARD, A. B., 1965. Quaternary of the southern Great Plains. In: H. E. WRIGHT, JR. and D. G. FREY (Editors), *Quaternary of the United States*. Princeton Univ. Press, Princeton, N.J., pp.203–216.

FRYE, J. C. and LEONARD, A. B., 1967. Buried soils, fossil mollusks, and Late Cenozoic paleoenvironments. In: *Essays in Paleontology and Stratigraphy—Dept. Geol., Univ. Kansas, Spec. Publ.* 2: 429–444.

FRYE, J. C. and WILLMAN, H. B., 1960. Classification of the Wisconsin stage in the Lake Michigan glacial lobe. *Illinois, Geol. Surv., Circ.*, 285: 16 pp.

FUCHS, V. E. and PATTERSON, T. T., 1947. The relation of volcanicity and orogeny to climatic change. *Geol. Mag.*, 8: 84.

GAGEL, C., 1923. Das Klima der Diluvialzeit. *Z. Deut. Geol. Ges.*, 75.

GALLOWAY, R. W., 1965. Late Quaternary climates in Australia. *J. Geol.*, 73: 603–618.

GALLOWAY, R. W., 1966. Palaeoclimatic evidence from Lake George. In: *Summary of Symposium on Lake George—Geol. Soc. Australia.*

GERASIMOV, I. P., 1930. On the post-Tertiary deposits in the western part of Low Turkestan. *Com. Géol. Léningrad, Bull.*, 49: 1067–1088.

GEYH, M. A., 1965. Proportional counter equipment for sample dating with ages exceeding 60,000 B.P., without enrichment. In: *Abstr. Intern. C¹⁴ Tritium Dating Conf., Washington State Univ.*, 102: 29–35.

GIBBS, J. A., 1962. Liquid scintillation counting of natural radiocarbon. *Packard Tech. Bull.* 8, La Grange, Ill., 15 pp.

GILBERT, G. K., 1890. Lake Bonneville. *U.S., Geol. Surv., Monographs*, 1: 438 pp.

GOLD, T., 1955. Instability of the earth's axis of rotation. *Nature*, 175: 526–529.

GOLDBERG, E. D. and GRIFFIN, J. J., 1964. Sedimentation rates and mineralogy in the South Atlantic. *J. Geophys. Res.*, 69: 4293–4309.

GOODWIN, H., 1962. Half-life of radiocarbon. *Nature*, 195: 943–984.

GRAHMANN, R., 1937. Die Entwicklungsgeschichte des Kaspisees und des Schwarzen Meeres. *Mitt. Ges. Erdk. Leipzig*, 54: 26–47.

GREEN, F. E., 1962. Additional notes on prehistoric wells at the Clovis Site. *Am. Antiquity*, 28: 230–234.

GREEN, F. E., 1963. The Clovis blades: an important addition to the Llano complex. *Am. Antiquity*, 29: 145–165.

GREEN, F. E., 1964. The Lubbock reservoir site. *West Texas Museum Bull.*, 85–123.

GRIFFIN, J. B., 1965. Late Quaternary prehistory in the northeastern Woodlands. In: H. E. WRIGHT, JR. and D. G. FREY (Editors), *The Quaternary of the United States*, Princeton Univ. Press, Princeton, N.J., pp.655–667.

GROSSCUP, G. R., 1956. The archeology of the Carson Sink area. *Univ. Calif. Archeol. Surv. Rept.*, 33: 58–64.

GROVE, A. T., 1958. The ancient erg of Hausaland and similar formations on the south side of the Sahara. *Geograph. J.*, 124: 528–533.

GROVE, A. T. and PULLAN, R. A., 1963. Some aspects of the Pleistocene paleogeography of the Chad Basin. *Viking Fund Anthropol.*, 36: 230–245.

HACK, J. T., 1941. Dunes of the western Navajo Country. *Geograph. Rev.*, 31: 240–263.

HAFSTEN, M., 1961. Pleistocene development of vegetation and climate in the southern High Plains as evidenced by pollen analysis. In: *Paleoecology of the Llano Estacado*. Museum of New Mexico Press, Santa Fe, pp.59–91.

HAGEM, O., 1917. Furnes og granens frozentning i Norge nedd. *Uestid. Forstl. Forsoksst.*, 1.

HARBECK JR., G. E., 1955. The effect of salinity on evaporation. *U.S., Geol. Surv., Profess. Papers*, 272-A: 6 pp.

HARBECK JR., G. E., KOHLER, M. A. and KOBERG, G. E., 1958. Water-loss investigations: Lake Meade studies. *U.S., Geol. Surv., Profess. Papers*, 298: 100 pp.

HARDING, S. T., 1935. Changes in lake levels in the Great Basin area. *Civil Eng. (N.Y.)*, 5: 87–92.

HARDING, S. T., 1942. Lakes. In: O. E. MEINZER (Editor), *Hydrology*, McGraw-Hill, New York, N.Y., pp.220–243.

HARDMAN, G. and VENSTROM, C., 1941. A one-hundred-year record of Truckee River runoff estimated from changes in levels and volumes of Pyramid and Winnemucca lakes. *Trans. Am. Geophys, Union*, 22: 71–90.

HARMER, F. W., 1901. Influence of the winds upon climate during the Pleistocene Epoch. *Geol. Soc. London*, 57: 405–476.

HARPER, W. G., 1957. Morphology and genesis of Calcisols. *Soil Sci.*, 21: 420–424.

HARRIS, A. H. and FINDLEY, J. S., 1963. Pleistocene-Recent fauna of the Isleta Caves, Bernalillo County, New Mexico. *Am. J. Sci.*, 262: 114–120.

HAURY, E. W., 1960. Association of fossil fauna and artifacts of the Sulphur Spring stage, Cochise culture. *Am. Antiquity*, 25: 609–610.

HAWLEY, J. W., and WILSON, W. E., 1965. Quaternary geology of the Winnemucca area, Nevada. *Desert Resch. Inst., Univ. Nevada, Tech. Rept.* 5: 94 pp.

HAY, O. P., 1923. Pleistocene of North America and its vertebrated animals from the states east of the Mississippi River. *Carnegie Inst. Wash. Publ.*, 322: 499 pp.

HAY, O. P., 1924. The Pleistocene of the middle region of North America and its vertebrated animals. *Carnegie Inst. Wash., Publ.*, 322A: 385 pp.

HAY, O. P., 1926. A collection of Pleistocene vertebrates from southwestern Texas. *U.S. Natl. Mus. Proc.*, 68: 1–18.

HEDEN, S., 1904. *Scientific Results of a Journey in Central Asia, 1899–1902.* Stockholm, Sweden, 1: 529 pp.

HELLAND, A., 1912. Traegraendser og sommervarmen. *Tidskrifter Skogbruk*, 20: 131, 305.

HESTER, J. J., 1960. Late Pleistocene extinction and radiocarbon dating. *Am. Antiquity*, 26: 58–77.

HESTER, J. J. and SCHOENWETTER, J., 1964. The reconstruction of past environments. *Fort Burgwin Res. Center*, 3: 89 pp.

HEVLY, R. H. and MARTIN, P. S., 1961. Geochronology of pluvial Lake Cochise, Southern Arizona. Pollen analysis of shore deposits. *J. Ariz. Acad. Sci.*, 2: 24–31.

HIBBARD, C. W., 1941. New mammals from the Rexroad fauna, Upper Pliocene of Kansas. *Am. Midland Naturalist*, 26: 337–368.

HIBBARD, C. W., 1944. Stratigraphy and vertebrate paleontology of Pleistocene deposits of south-western Kansas. *Bull. Geol. Soc. Am.*, 55: 707–754.

HIBBARD, C. W., 1949. Pleistocene vertebrate paleontology in North America. *Bull. Geol. Soc. Am.*, 60: 1417–1428.

HIBBARD, C. W., 1960. An interpretation of Pliocene and Pleistocene climates in North America. *Mich. Acad. Sci., Ann. Rept.*, 62: 5–30.

HIBBARD, C. W., 1963. A late Illinoian fauna from Kansas and its climatic significance. *Mich. Acad. Sci. Paper*, 48: 187–221.

HIBBARD, C. W. and TAYLOR, D. W., 1960. The late Pleistocene faunas from southwestern Kansas. *Univ. Mich. Museum Paleontol. Contrib.*, 16: 1–223.

HIMPEL, K., 1947. Ein Beitrag zum Eiszeitproblem. *Z. Naturforsch*, 2.

HOGBOM, I., 1923. Ancient inland dunes of northern and middle Europe. *Geograph. Ann.*, 5: 113–242.

HOHN, M. H. and HELLERMAN, J., 1961. The diatoms. In: F. WENDORF (Editor), *Paleoecology of the Llano Estacado*. Museum New Mexico Press, Santa Fe, pp.98–104.

HOLM, D. A., 1953. Dome-shaped dunes of central Nejd, Saudia Arabia. *Congr. Géol. Intern., Compt. Rend., 19e, Algiers, 1952*, 7: 107–111.

HOLMES, A., 1960. A geological time scale. *Trans. Edinburgh Geol. Soc.*, 17: 183–216.

HOSHIAI, M. and KOBAYASHI, K., 1957. A theoretical discussion on the so-called "snow-line", with reference to the temperature during the last Glacial Age in Japan. *Jap. J. Geol. Geograph*, 28.

HOWARD, U., 1946. A review of the Pleistocene birds of Fossil Lake, Oregon. *Carn. Inst. Wash. Publ.*, 551: 141–195.

HOWELL, L. G., and MARTINEZ, H. D., 1957. Polar movements as indicated by rock magnetism. *Geophysics*, 22: 384–397.

HUBBS, C. L. and MILLER, R. R., 1948. The zoological evidence. In: *The Great Basin with Emphasis on Glacial and Post-glacial Times—Univ. Utah Bull.*, 38: 17–166.

HUNT, C. B., 1953. Pleistocene-recent boundary in the Rocky Mountain region. *U.S., Geol. Surv., Bull.*, 996-A: 25 pp.

HUNT, C. B., 1955. Radiocarbon dating in the light of stratigraphy and weathering. *Sci. Monthly*, 81: 240–247.

HUNTINGTON, E., 1906. Pangong: a glacial lake in the Tibetan Plateau. *J. Geol.*, 14: 599–617.

HUNTINGTON, E., 1907. Some characteristics of the glacial period in nonglaciated regions. *Bull. Geol. Soc. Am.*, 18: 351–388.

HUNTINGTON, E., 1914. The solar hypothesis of climatic changes. *Bull. Geol. Soc. Am.*, 25: 477–590.

HUNTINGTON, E. and VISHER, S. S., 1922. *Climatic Changes, Their Nature and Cause*. Yale Univ. Press, New Haven, Conn., 329 pp.

HUTCHINSON, G. E., 1939. Ecological observations on the fishes of Kashmir and Indian Tibet. *Ecol. Mon.*, 9: 145–182.

IVES, J., 1803. *Garianonum the Romans*. Downes, Yarmouth, 54 pp.

IVES, R. L., 1940. An astronomical hypothesis to explain Permian glaciation. *J. Franklin Inst.*, 230.

JAEGER, F., 1926. Forschungen über das diluviale Klima in Mexiko. *Petermans Mitt. Ergänzungshefte*, 190: 64 S.

JAEGER, F., 1939. Die Trockenseen der Erde. *Petermans Mitt. Ergänzungshefte*, 236: 159 S.

JAMIESON, T. F., 1863. On the parallel roads of Glen Roxy and their place in the history of the glacial period. *Quart. J. Geol. Soc. London*, 19: 235–259.

JARDETZKY, W. S., 1961. Investigations of Milankovitch and the Quaternary curve of effective solar radiation. *Ann. N. Y. Acad. Sci.*, 95: 418–423.

JELGERSMA, S. and PANNEKOEK, A. J., 1960. Post-glacial rise of sea level in the Netherlands. *Geol. Mijnbouw*, 39: 201–207.

JONES, J. P., 1914. The tufa deposits of the Salton Sink. In: D. J. MACDOUGAL (Editor), *Salton Sea—Carnegie Inst. Wash. Publ.*, 193: 79–83.

JONES, J. P., 1925. The geologic history of Lake Lahontan. *Carnegie Inst. Wash. Publ.*, 352: 1–50.

KAISER, K., 1960. Klimazeugen des periglazialen Dauerfrostbodens in Mittel und Westeuropa. *Eiszeitalter Gegenwart*, 11: 121–141.

KARLSTROM, T. N. V., 1961. The glacial history of Alaska: its bearing on paleoclimatic theory. *Ann. N.Y. Acad. Sci.* 95: 290–340.

KAUFMAN, A. and BROECKER, W., 1965. Comparison of Th [230] and C[14] ages for carbonate materials from Lakes Lahontan and Bonneville. *J. Geophys. Res.*, 70: 4039–4054.

KAY, G. F., 1931. Classification and duration of the Pleistocene period. *Bull. Geol. Soc. Am.*, 42: 425–466.

KEBLE, R. A., 1947. Notes on Australian Quaternary climates and migration. *Natl. Museum Victoria, Mem.*, 15: 28–81.

KEITH, M. L. and WEBER, J. N., 1964. Carbon and oxygen isotopic composition of selected limestones and fossils. *Geochim. Cosmochim. Acta*, 28: 1787–1816.

KEITH, M. L., ANDERSON, G. M. and EICHLER, R., 1964. Carbon and oxygen isotopic composition of mollusk shells from marine and fresh-water environments. *Geochim. Cosmochim. Acta*, 28: 1757–1786.

KESTNER, F., 1962. The old coastline of The Wash. *Wash. Geograph. J.*, 128: 455–478.

KING, L. C., 1961. The palaeoclimatology of Gondwanaland during the Paleozoic and Mesozoic Eras. In A. E. M. NAIRN (Editor), *Descriptive Palaeoclimatology*. Interscience, New York, N.Y., pp.307–331.

KLUTE, F., 1921. Über die Ursachen der letzten Eiszeit. *Geograph. Z.*, 27: 199–203.

KLUTE, F., 1928. Die Bedeutung der Depression der Schneegrenze für eiszeitliche Probleme. *Z. Gletscherk.*, 16: 70–93.

KLUTE, F., 1930. Verschiebung der klimage Brete der letzten Eiszeit. *Petermans Mitt. Erganzungs-heft*, 209: 166–182.

KOEPPE, C. E. and DE LONG, G. C., 1958. *Weather and Climate.* McGraw-Hill, New York, N.Y., 341 pp.

KOHLER, M. A., NORDENSON, T. J. and BAKER, D. R., 1959. Evaporation maps for the United States. *U.S. Dept. Commerce Tech. Paper*, 37: 13 pp.

KÖPPEN, W., 1920. Die Lufttemperatur und der Schneegrenze. *Petermans Mitt.*, 66: 78–80.

KÖPPEN, W. and WEGENER, A., 1924. *Die Klimate der Geologischen Vorzeit.* Borntraeger, Berlin, 256 S.

KORN, H., 1938a. Stratification and absolute time ground building and sedimentation rate in a varied trough from the Thuringian French Lower Carboniferous and Upper Devonian. *Neues Jahrb. Mineral. Geol. Paläontol.*, 74A: 50–186.

KORN, H., 1938b. Schichtung und absolute Zeit. *Neues Jahrb. Mineral. Geol. Paläontol.*, 74.

KOSTER, R., 1960. Zur frage der gegenwärtigen Senkung der schleswig-holsteinishen Ostküste. *Kuste*, 8: 139–159.

KRAUS, E. B., 1961. Physical aspects of deduced and actual climatic change. *Ann., N.Y. Acad. Sci.*, 95: 225–234.

KRIGE, L. J., 1929. Magmatic cycles, continental drift and ice ages. *Proc. Geol. Soc. S. Africa* 32: 21–40.

KROOK, M., 1953. Interstellar matter and the solar constant. In: H. SHAPLEY (Editor), *Climatic Change, Evidence, Causes, and Effects.* Harvard Univ. Press, Cambridge, Mass., pp.143–146.

KU, T. L. and BROECKER, W. S., 1966. Atlantic deep-sea stratigraphy: extension of absolute chronology to 320,000 years. *Science*, 151: 448–450.

KUKLA, J., VOJEN, L. and QUIDO, Z., 1961. Zur stratigraphie der lösse in der tschecho-slowakei. *Quartär*, 13: 1–29.

KULP, J. L., FEELY, H. W. and TRYON, L. W., 1951. Lamont natural radiocarbon measurements, 1. *Science*, 114: 565–568.

LAMB, H. H., 1964. The role of atmosphere and oceans in relation to climatic changes and the growth of ice sheets on land. In: A. NAIRN (Editor), *Problems in Palaeoclimatology*, Interscience, London, pp.332–348.

LANCE, J. F., 1959. Fauna remains from the Lehner Mammoth Site. *Am. Antiquity*, 25: 35–39.

LANGBEIN, W. B., 1949. Annual runoff in the United States. *U.S., Geol. Surv., Circ.*, 52: 14 pp.

LANGBEIN, W. B., 1961. Salinity and hydrology of closed lakes. *U.S., Geol. Surv., Profess. Papers*, 412: 20 pp.

LAROQUE, A., 1966. Pleistocene mollusca of Ohio. *Dept. Nat. Resources Bull.*, 62 (1): 111 pp.

LARTET, L., 1865. Sur la formation du bassin de la Mer Morte on lac asphaltite, et sur les changements survenus dans le niteau de ce lac. *Compt. Rendu.*, 60: 796–800.

LAUDERMILK, J. D. and MUNZ, P. A., 1934. Plants in the dung of *Nothrotherinns* from Gypsum Cave, Nevada. *Carnegie Inst. Wash. Publ.*, 433: 29–37.

LAWRENCE, D. B., 1950. Glacier fluctuation for six centuries in southeastern Alaska and its relation to solar activity. *Geograph. Rev.*, 40: 191–223.

LAWRENCE, D. B., 1966. Recent variations in glaciers and closed-basin lakes-indications of climatic change. *33rd J. W. Powell Mem. Lecture, 42nd Ann. Meeting, Am. Assoc. Adv. Sci.*

LAWRENCE, D. B. and LAWRENCE, E. B., 1961. Response of enclosed lakes to current glaciopluvial climatic conditions in middle latitude western North America. *Ann. N.Y. Acad. Sci.*, 95: 341–356.

LAWRENCE, D. B. and LAWRENCE, E. B., 1965. Glacial studies in New Zealand. *Mazamas*, 47: 17–27.

LEAKEY, L. S. B., 1930. East African lakes. *Geograph. J.*, 77: 497–514.

LEE, C. H., 1927. Discussion of "Evaporation on Reclamation Projects" by I. E. Honk. *Trans. Am. Soc. Civil Eng.*, 90: 340–343.

LEIBNITZ, G. W., 1706. Note in *Historie des Sci.*, 1706: 9–11.

LEOPOLD, L. B., 1951. Pleistocene climate in New Mexico. *Am. J. Sci.*, 249: 152–168.

LEVERETT, F., 1929. Pleistocene glaciations of the northern hemisphere. *Science*, 69: 231–239.

LIBBY W. F., 1951. Radiocarbon dates, 2. *Science*, 114: 291–296.

LIBBY, W. F., 1952. *Radiocarbon Dating*. Chicago Univ. Press, Chicago, Ill., 124 pp.

LIBBY, W. F., 1955. *Radiocarbon Dating*. 2 ed., Chicago Univ. Press, Chicago, Ill., 175 pp.

LIBBY, W. F., ANDERSON, E. C. and ARNOLD, J. R., 1949. Age determination by radiocarbon content: worldwide assay of natural radiocarbon. *Science*, 109: 227.

LLOYD, R. M., 1964. Variations in the oxygen and carbon isotope ratios of Florida Bay mollusks and their environmental significance. *J. Geol.*, 72: 84–111.

LONGINELLI, A. and TOGLIATTI, V., 1962. Composizione isotopica dell'ossigeno di una fauna aechinidi dell'Atlantico nord-occidentale. *Atti Soc. Toscana Sci. Nat. Pisa. Proc. Verbali Mem., Ser. A*, 2: 1–8.

LOUIS, H., 1926. The distribution of glacial forms in the western United States. *Z. Geomorphol.*, 2: 221–235.

LOUIS, H., 1934. Glazialmorphologische studien in den gebirgen der Britischen Inseln. *Berlin Geograph. Arb.*, 6.

LOUIS, H., 1938. Eiszeitliche seen in anatolien. *Z. Ges. Erdkunde*, 1938: 267–285.

LOWENSTAM, H. A., 1961. O^{18}/O^{16} ratios, and strontium and magnesium contents of recent and fossil brachipods and their bearing on the history of the oceans. *J. Geol.*, 69: 241–260.

LOWENSTAM, H. A. and EPSTEIN, S., 1954. Paleotemperatures of the post-Aptian Cretaceous as determined by the oxygen isotope method. *J. Geol.*, 62: 207–248.

LUNDELIUS, E., 1964. The use of vertebrates in paleoecological reconstructions. In: J. H. HESTER and J. SCHOENWETTER (Editors), *Reconstruction of Past Environments—Fort Burgwin Res. Center, Conf. Paleoecol.*, 1962, pp.26–31.

LYELL, C., 1830–1833. *Principles of Geology*. Murray, London; 1: 511 pp.; 2: 330 pp.; 3: 398 pp.

LYELL, C., 1839. *Nouveaux Elements de Géologie*. Pitois-Levrault, Paris, 648 pp.

LYELL, C., 1873. *The Geological Evidences of the Antiquity of Man*, 4 ed. Murray, London, 572 pp.

MABEY, D. R., 1956. Geophysical studies in southern California basins. *Geophysics*, 21: 839–853.

MACKENZIE, L. A., 1946. *Report on the Kalahari Expedition, 1945*. Govt. Printer, Pretoria, 35 pp.

MADIGAN, C. T., 1936. The Australian sand-ridge deserts. *Geograph.*, Rev. 26: 205–227.

MALDE, H. E., 1964. Environment and man in arid America. *Science*, 145: 123–129.

MANLEY, G., 1955. A climatological survey of the retreat of the Laurentide ice sheet. *Am. J. Sci.*, 256–273.

MANN, P., 1966. Geophysical investigation of Lake George. In: *Summary of Symposium on Lake George*. Geol. Soc. Australia, Geol. Soc. Australia, Canberra, 3 pp.

MARTIN, P. S., 1963a. *The Last 10,000 Years*. Univ. Ariz. Press, Tucson, Ariz., 87 pp.

MARTIN, P. S., 1963b. Early man in Arizona: the pollen evidence. *Am. Antiquity*, 29: 67–73.

MARTIN, P. S., SCHOENWETTER, J. and ARMS, B. C., 1961. *Southwestern Palynology and Prehistory. The Last 10,000 Years*. Univ. Ariz. Press, Tucson, Ariz., 119 pp.

MCCREA, J. M., 1950. On the isotopic chemistry of carbonates and a paleotemperature scale. *J, Chem. Phys.*, 18: 849–857.

MCFARLAN JR. E., 1961. Radiocarbon dating of late Quaternary deposits, south Louisiana. *Bull. Geol. Soc. Am.*, 72: 129–158.

MEADE, G. E., 1944. The Blanco-fauna. *Univ. Texas Publ.*, 4401: 509–542.

MEHRINGER JR. P. H. and HAYNES, C. V., JR., 1965. The pollen evidence for the environment of early man and extinct mammals at the Lehner Mammoth site, southeastern Arizona. *Am. Antiquity*, 31: 17–23.

MELTON, F. A., 1940. A tentative classification of sand dunes-its application to dune history in the Southern High Plains. *J. Geol.*, 48: 113–174.

MELTON, M. A., 1965. The geomorphic and paleoclimatic significance of alluvial deposits in southern Arizona. *J. Geol.*, 73: 1–38.

MEINZER, O. E., 1922. Map of Pleistocene lakes of the basin-and-range province and its significance. *Bull. Geol. Soc. Am.*, 33: 541–552.

MENZEL, D. H., 1953. On the causes of the Ice Ages. In: H. SHAPLEY (Editor), *Climatic Change, Evidence, Causes, and Effects*. Harvard Univ. Press, Cambridge, Mass., pp.117–121.

METEOROLOGICAL DIVISION, 1944. Meteorology of the Canadian Arctic. *Can. Dept. Transport, Meteorol. Div.*, 85 pp.

MIKI, S., 1956. Remains of *Pinus koraiensis* and associated remains in Japan. *Botan. Mag.*, 89.

MILANKOVITCH, M., 1930. Mathematische Klimalehre und astronomische Theorie der Klima-schwankunge. *Handbuch Klimatol.*, 1: 176 S.

MILANKOVITCH, M., 1938. Astronomische Mittel zur Erforschung der erdgeschichtlichen Klimate. *Handbuch Geophys.*, 9: 593–698.

MILANKOVITCH, M., 1941. *Kanon der Erdestrahlung und seine Anwendung auf das Eiszeitproblem.* Roy. Serbian Acad., Belgrade, 133 S.

MILLER, D. W., GERAGHTY, J. J. and COLLINS, R. S., 1963. *Water Atlas of the United States.* Water Inform. Center, Port Washington, N.Y., 40 pp.

MILLER, M. M., 1967. Alaska's mighty rivers of ice. *Natl. Geograph.*, 131: 195–217.

MITCHELL JR., J. M., 1961. Recent secular changes of global temperature. *Ann. N.Y. Acad. Sci.*, 95: 235–250.

MITCHELL JR., J. M., 1965. Theoretical, paleoclimatology. In: H. E. WRIGHT and D. G. FREY (Editors), *Quaternary of the United States.* Princeton Univ. Press, Princeton, N.J., 881–901.

MORAWETZ, S., 1955. Zur Frage der uszeitlichen Temperaturniederung. *Geograph. Ges. Wien, Mitt.*, 97: 192–206.

MORRISON, R. B., 1958. Geology of Hidden Cave, near Fallon, Nevada. *Great Basin Archeol. Congr., 5th, 1958, Proc.*

MORRISON, R. B., 1964a. Lake Lahontan: geology of southern Carson Desert, Nevada. *U.S. Geol. Surv., Profess. Papers*, 401: 156 pp.

MORRISON, R. B., 1964b. *Soil Stratigraphy: Principles, Applications to Differentiation and Correlation of Quaternary Deposits and Landforms, and Applications to Soil Science. Thesis*, Univ. Nevada, Reno, Nev., 178 pp. (unpublished).

MORRISON, R. B., 1965a. Quaternary geology of the Great Basin. In: H. E. WRIGHT, JR. and D. G. FREY (Editors), *Quaternary of the United States.* Princeton Univ. Press, Princeton, N.J., pp.265–285.

MORRISON, R. B., 1965b. A suggested Pleistocene-Recent (Holocene) boundary for the Great Basin Region of the western U.S.A. In: *Rept. Intern. Congr. Quaternary, Lodz, 6th, 1961*, 463–466.

MORRISON, R. B., 1966. Predecessors of Great Salt Lake. In: *The Great Salt Lake—Utah, Geol. Surv. Guidebook*, 20: 77–104.

MORRISON, R. B. and FRYE, J. C., 1965. Correlation of the middle and late Quaternary successions of the Lake Lahontan, Lake Bonneville, Rocky Mountain (Wasatch Range), southern Great Plains, and eastern Midwest areas. *Nevada, Bureau Mines, Rept.*, 9: 45 pp.

MORTENSEN, H., 1952. Heutiger Firnrückgang und Eiszeitklima. *Erdkunde*, 6: 145–160.

MULLER, R. R., 1945. Four new species of fossil cyprinedont fishes from eastern California. *Proc. Wash. Acad. Sci.*, 35: 316–321.

MUNK, W. H. and MARKOWITZ, W., 1960. North pole drifts 6 inches each year. *N. Y. Times*, August 1, 1960.

NAIDIN, D. P., TEIS, R. V. and CHUPAKHIN, M. A., 1956. The Cretaceous Crimean fauna. *Geokhimiya*, 8: 752.

NILSSON, E., 1931. Quaternary glaciations and pluvial lakes in British East Africa. *Geograph. Ann.*, 13: 249–349.

NILSSON, E., 1938. Pluvial lakes in East Africa. *Geol. Foren., Stockholm, Forhandl.*, 60: 423–433.

NILSSON, E., 1940. Ancient changes of climate in British East Africa and Abyssinia. *Geograph. Ann.*, 22: 1–79.

NILSSON, E., 1953. Om södra Sveriges senkvartara historia. *Geol. Foren. Stockholm Forh.*, 75: 155–246.

NORRIS, R., 1948. Evaporation from extensive surfaces of water roughened by waves. *Quart J. Roy. Meteorol. Soc.*, 74: 1–12.

ODUM, H. T., 1952. The Carolina bays and a Pleistocene weather map. *Am. J. Sci.*, 250: 263–270.

OLDFIELD, F. and SCHOENWETTER, J., 1964. Late Quaternary environments and early man on the Southern High Plains. *Am. Antiquity*, 38: 226–229.

OLSON, E. A., 1963. Columbia Univ., New York, N.Y. (unpublished).

OLSON, E. A. and BROECKER, W. S., 1958. Sample contamination and reliability of radiocarbon dates. *Trans. N.Y. Acad. Sci., Ser. 2*, 20: 593–604.

OPDYKE, N. D., 1962. Paleoclimatology and continental drift. In: S. K. RUNCORN (Editor), *Continental Drift.* Acad. Press, New York, N.Y., pp.41–65.

ÖPIK, E. J., 1950. Secular changes of stellar structure and the Ice Ages. *Armagh Obs., Contrib.*, 5.
ÖPIK, E. J., 1953. A climatological and astronomical interpretation of the ice ages and of the past variations of terrestrial climate. *Armagh Obs., Contrib.*, 9: 79 pp.
ÖPIK, E. J., 1958a. Climate and the changing sun. *Sci. Am.*, 198: 85–92.
ÖPIK, E. J., 1958b. Solar variability and paleoclimatic changes. *Irish Astron. J.*, 5: 97–109.

PANOFSKY, H. A., 1956. Theories of climatic change. *Weatherwise*, 9: 183–187, 204.
PARKER, F., 1958. Eastern Mediterranean foraminifera. *Rept. Swedish Deep-Sea Expedition*, 8: 4.
PARRY, W. T. and REEVES JR., C. C., 1967. Preliminary report: soft sediment dolomite from pluvial Lake Mound, Texas. *Texas J. Sci.*, 19: 132–137.
PEARSON JR., F. J., 1965. Use of C^{13}/C^{12} ratios to correct radiocarbon ages of materials initially diluted by limestone. In: *Abstr. Intern. C^{14} Tritium Dating Conf.*,—Wash. State Univ., Seattle, Wash., pp.357–366.
PENCK, A., 1914. The shifting of the climatic belts. *Scottish Geograph. Mag.*, 30: 281–293.
PENCK, A., 1928. Die ursachen der eiszert. *Sitzungsber. Akad. Wiss. Phys. Match.*, 6: 76–85.
PENCK, A., 1931. Zentral-Asien. *Z. Ges. Erdk.*, 1931: 1–13.
PENCK, A., 1932. Palaok limatologie. *Geograf. Z.*, 38: 466–484.
PENCK, A., 1936. Europe zur letzten Eiszeit. In: *Landerkundliche Forschung—Festschrift Norbert Krebs*. Engelhorns, Stuttgart, S.222–237.
PENCK, A., 1938. Die Strahlungskurve und die geologische Zeitrechnung. *Z. Ges. Erdk.*, 1938: 231–250.
PENMAN, H. L., 1955. Evaporation from Lake Eyre. In: *Lake Eyre, South Australia, The Great Flooding of 1949–1950*. Roy. Geograph. Soc. Australasia, S. Australian Branch, Adelaide, pp. 57–61.
PETERSON, M. N. A., BEIN, G. S. and BERNER, R. A., 1963. Radiocarbon studies of recent dolomite from Deep Spring Lake, California. *J. Geophys. Res.*, 68: 6493–6505.
PFELLER, R. L., 1964. The global atmospheric circulation. *Trans. N.Y. Acad. Sci.*, 26: 984–997.
PILGRIM, L., 1904. Versuch einer rechnerischen Behandlung des Eiszeitproblems. *Wurtt. Verhandl.*, 60: 26–117.
PIRENNE, H., 1958. *A History of Europe, 1*. Anchor Books, Doubleday, New York, N.Y., 282 pp.
PLASS, G. N., 1956. The carbon dioxide theory of climatic change. *Tellus*, 8: 140–154.
PLASS, G. N., 1961. The influence of infrared absorptive molecules on the climate. *Ann. N.Y. Acad. Sci.*, 95: 61–71.
POOLE, F. G., 1957. Paleowind directions in late Paleozoic and early Mesozoic time on the Colorado Plateau as determined by cross strata. *Bull. Geol. Soc. Am.*, 688: 1870 (abstract).
POOLE, F. G., 1961. Stream directions in Triassic rocks on the Colorado Plateau. In: *Short Papers in the Geologic and Hydrologic Sciences— U.S., Geol. Surv., Profess. Papers*, 424–C: 139.
POOLE, F. G., 1962. Wind directions in late Paleozoic to middle Mesozoic time on the Colorado Plateau. In: Short papers in geology, hydrology, and topography. *U.S., Geol. Surv., Profess. Papers*, 450D: 147.
POOLE, F. G., 1963. Paleowinds in Paleoclimatology. In: A. E. M. NAIRN (Editor), *Problems in Palaeoclimatology*. Interscience, London, pp.394–405.
POSER, H., 1951. Die Nördliche Lössgrenze in Mitteleuropa. *Eiszeitalter Gegenwart*, 1: 27–55.
POTTER, P. E., SHIMP, N. F. and WITTERS, J., 1963. Trace elements in marine and fresh-water argillaceous sediments. *Geochim. Cosmochim. Acta*, 27: 669–694.
POTZGER, J. E. and THARP, B. C., 1943. Pollen record of Canadian spruce and fir from Texas bog. *Science*, 98: 584–585.
POTZGER, J. E. and THARP, B. C., 1947. Pollen profile from a Texas bog. *Ecology*, 28: 274–280.
POTZGER, J. E. and THARP, B. C., 1954. Pollen study of two bogs in Texas. *Ecology*, 35: 462–466.
POURADE, R. F. (Editor), 1966. *Ancient Hunters of the Far West*. Union-Tribune Publ. Co., San Diego, Calif., 208 pp.
PRICE, W. A., 1958. Sedimentology and Quaternary geomorphology of south Texas. *Trans., Gulf Coast Assoc. Geol. Soc.*, 8: 41–75.
PRINZ, G., 1909. Die Vergletscherung des nördlichen Teiles des zentralen Tien-schan-Gebirges. *Kgl. Keizerl. Geograph. Ges., Mitt.*, 52: 10–75.
PUMPELLY, R., 1905. Explorations in Turkestan. *Carnegie Inst. Wash. Publ.*, 26: 324 pp.

QUEZEL, P. and MARTINEZ, C., 1961. Le dernier interpluvial au Sahara central: essai de chronologie palynologique et paleochimatique. *Libyca*, 6/7: 211–227.

QUINN, J. H., 1958. Plateau surfaces of the Ozarks. *Proc. Arkansas Acad. Sci.*, 11: 36–44.

QUINN, J. H., 1961. Prairie mounds of Arkansas. *Arkansas Archeol. Soc.*, 2: 1–8.

QUINN, J. H., 1965. Monadnocks, divides, and Ozark physiography. *Proc. Arkansas Acad. Sci.*, 19: 90–97.

QUINN, J. H., 1966. Pleistocene climates. *Geol. Soc. Am., Southeastern Sect., Ann. Meeting, Abstr.*, pp.37–38.

RAMSAY, W., 1910. Orogensis und Klima. *Overs. Finska Vet. Soc. Förh.*, 52.

RANGE, P., 1923. Über das spätglaziale Klima. *Z. Deut. Geol. Ges.*, 75.

RANKAMA, K., 1963. *Progress in Isotope Geology*. Interscience, London, 705 pp.

REEVES JR., C. C., 1965a. Pluvial lakes and Pleistocene climate on the Southern High Plains, Texas. *Great Plains, J.*, 5: 44–50.

REEVES JR., C. C., 1965b. Pluvial Lake Palomas, northwestern Chihuahua, Mexico, and Pleistocene geologic history of south central New Mexico. *Guidebook 16th Ann. Field Conf., New Mexico Geol. Soc.*, pp.199–203.

REEVES JR., C. C., 1965c. Pleistocene climate of the Llano Estacado. *J. Geol.*, 73: 181–189.

REEVES JR., C. C., 1965d. Chronology of West Texas pluvial lake dunes. *J. Geol.*, 73: 504–508.

REEVES JR., C. C., 1966a. Pluvial lake basins of West Texas. *J. Geol.*, 74: 269–291.

REEVES JR., C. C., 1966b. Pleistocene climate of the Llano Estacado, 2. *J. Geol.*, 74: 642–647.

REEVES JR., C. C., and PARRY, W. T., 1965. Geology of West Texas pluvial lake carbonates. *Am. J. Sci.*, 263: 606–615.

REICHE, P., 1938. An analysis of cross-laminations in the Coconino Sandstone. *J. Geol.*, 43: 905.

REID, E. M. and CHANDLER, M. E. J., 1933. *The London Clay Flora*. Brit. Mus. Nat. History, London.

REYNOLDS, R. C., 1965. The concentration of boron in Precambrian seas. *Geochim. Cosmochim. Acta*, 29: 1–16.

RICHMOND, G. M., 1965. Glaciation of the Rocky Mountains. In: H. E. WRIGHT, JR. and D. G. FREY (Editors), *The Quaternary of the United States*. Princeton Univ. Press, N.J., pp.217–223.

RICHTER-BERNBURG, G., 1957. Isochrone Warven im Anhydrit des Zechstein, 2. *Geol. Jahrb.*, 74: 601–610.

RICHTER-BERNBURG, G., 1958. Die korrelierung isochroner Warven im Anhydrit des Zechstein, 2. *Geol. Jahrb.*, 75: 629–639.

RICHTER-BERNBURG, G., 1960. Zeitmessung geologischer Vorgänge nach Warven-Korrelationen im Zechstein. *Geol. Rundschau*, 49: 132–148.

RIEDEL, W. R., BRAMLETTE, M. N. and PARKER, F. L., 1963. Boundary in deep-sea sediments. *Science*, 140: 1238.

ROGERS, A. W., 1922. Post-Cretaceous climates of South Africa. *S. African. J. Sci.*, 19: 1–31.

ROHWER, C., 1931. Evaporation from free water surfaces. *U.S. Dept., Agr., Tech. Bull.*, 271: 96 pp.

ROHWER, C., 1934. Evaporation from different types of pans. *Am. Soc. Civil Eng.*, 99: 673–703.

ROOSMA, A., 1958. A climate record from Searles Lake, California. *Science*, 128: 716 (abstract).

ROSCOE, E. J., 1963. Stratigraphic summary of Quaternary Bonneville basin mollusca. *Sterkiana*, 9: 1–23.

ROUND, F. E., 1961. Diatoms from Esthwaite. *New Phytologist*, 60: 43–59.

RUNCORN, S. K., 1956. Paleomagnetic survey in Arizona and Utah. *Bull. Geol., Soc. Am.*, 67: 301–316.

RUNCORN, S. K., 1962. Paleomagnetic evidence for continental drift and its geophysical cause. In: S. K. RUNCORN (Editor), *Continental Drift*, Acad. Press, New York, N.Y., pp.1–40.

RUSSELL, I. C., 1885. Geological history of Lake Lahontan, a Quaternary lake of northwestern Nevada. *U.S., Geol. Surv., Monograph*, 2: 288 pp.

RUSSELL, I. C., 1889. Quaternary history of Mono Valley, California. *U.S., Geol., Surv., 8th Ann. Rept., 1886–1887*, 1: 261–394.

RUSSELL, I. C., 1893. A geologic reconnaissance in central Washington. *U.S., Geol. Surv., Bull.*, 108: 108 pp.

SACKETT, W. M., 1960. Protactinium-231 content of ocean water and sediments. *Science*, 132: 1761–1762.

SACKETT, W. M., 1965. Deposition rates by the protactinium method. Symposium on Marine Geochemistry. *Univ. Rhode Islands, Occas. Publ.*, 3: 29–40.

SAUER, C. O., 1950. Grassland climax, fire, and man. *J. Range Management*, 3: 16–22.

SAYLES, E. B. and ANTEVS, E., 1941. The Cochise culture. *Medallion Papers*, 29: 1–81.

SCHAFER, J. P., 1949. Some periglacial features in central Montana. *J. Geol.*, 57: 154.

SCHAEFER, V. J., 1950. Experimental meteorology. *J. Appl. Math. Phys.*, 1: 153.

SCHELL, W. R., FAIRHALL, A. W. and HARP, G. D., 1965. Measurement of C^{14} in known age samples and their geophysical implications. *Intern. Conf. Radiocarbon Tritium Dating*. Wash. State Univ., Seattle, Wash., 784 pp.

SCHNELL, I. I., 1961. Recent evidence about the nature of climate changes and its implications. *N.Y. Acad. Sci. Ann.*, 95: 251–270.

SCHOLL, D. W., 1960. Pleistocene algal pinnacles at Searles Lake, California, *J. Sediment. Petrol.*, 30: 414–431.

SCHOLL, D. W., 1964. Recent sedimentary record in mangrove swamps and rise in sea level over the southwestern coast of Florida, 1. *Marine Geol.*, 2: 344–366.

SCHOLL, D. W. and STUIVER, M., 1967. Recent submergence of southern Florida: a comparison with adjacent coasts and other eustatic data. *Bull. Geol. Soc. Am.*, 78: 437–454.

SCHOVE, D. J., NAIRN, A. E. M. and OPDYKE, N. D., 1958. The climatic geography of the Permian. *Geograph. Ann.*, 40: 216–231.

SCHUMM, S. A., 1965. Quaternary Paleohydrology. In: H. E. WRIGHT JR. and D. G. FREY (Editors), *The Quaternary of the United States*. Princeton Univ. Press, Princeton, N.J., :783–794.

SCHWARZBACH, M., 1961a. *Das Klima Der Vorzeit*, 2 Aufl. Enke, Stuttgart.

SCHWARZBACH, M., 1961b. The climatic history of Europe and North America. In: A. E. M. NAIRN (Editor), *Descriptive Palaeoclimatology*. Interscience, New York, N.Y., pp.255–291.

SCHWARZBACH, M., 1963. *Climates of the Past: An Introduction to Paleoclimatology*. Van Nostrand, London, pp.388.

SCHWINNER, R., 1936. *Lehrbuch der Physikalischen Geologie*. Berlin.

SEARS, P. B., 1952. Palynology in southern North America, 1. Archeological horizons in the basins of Mexico. *Bull. Geol. Soc. Am.*, 63: 241–254.

SEARS, P. B., 1953. Climate and civilization. In: H. SHAPLEY (Editor), *Climatic Change, Evidence, Causes, and Effects*. Harvard Univ. Press., Cambridge, Mass., pp.35–50.

SEARS, P. B. and CLISBY, K. H., 1952. Two long climatic records. *Science*, 116: 176–178.

SEARS, P. B. and CLISBY, K. H., 1955. Pleistocene climate in Mexico. *Bull. Geol. Soc. Am.*, 66: 521–530.

SELLARDS, E. H., 1952. *Early Man in America*. Univ. Texas Press, Austin, Texas, 211 pp.

SELLERS, W. D., 1965. *Physical Climatology*. Univ. Chicago Press, Chicago, Ill., 272 pp.

SHAPLEY, H., 1953. On climate and life. In: H. SHAPLEY (Editor), *Climatic Change, Evidence, Causes, and Effects*. Harvard Univ. Press, Cambridge, Mass., 394 pp.

SHEPARD, T. P. and SUESS, H. E., 1956. Rate of post-glacial rise of sea level. *Science*, 123: 1082–1083.

SHOTTON, F. W., 1960. Large-scale patterned ground in the valley of Worcestershire. *Geol. Mag.*, 97: 404–409.

SIMONS, F. S., 1956. A note on Pur-purdune Viru Valley, Peru. *J. Geol.*, 64: 517–521.

SIMONSON, R. W., 1954. Identification and interpretation of buried soils. *Am. J. Sci.*, 252: 705–722.

SIMPSON, G. C., 1934. World climate during the Quaternary Period. *Quart. J. Roy. Meteorol. Soc.*, 60: 425–471.

SIMPSON, G., 1937. Ice Ages. *Proc. Roy. Inst.*, 30: 125–142.

SLAUGHTER, B. H. and HOOVER, B. R., 1963. The Sulphur River Formation and the mammals of the Ben Franklin local fauna. *J. Graduate Res. Center*, 31: 132–148.

SMILEY, T. L., 1955. Geochronology: with special reference to southwestern United States. *Univ. Arizona, Phys. Sci. Bull.*, 12: 200 pp.

SMITH, G. I. and HAINES, D. V., 1964. Character and distribution of nonclastic minerals in Searles Lake evaporite deposits. California. *U.S., Geol. Surv., Bull.*, 1181-P: 58 pp.

SMITH, H. T. U., 1938. Quaternary dune building in central Kansas. *Geol. Soc. Am., Proc.*, 1938: 115 (abstract).

SMITH, H. T. U., 1940. Geological studies in Southwestern Kansas. *Kansas, Geol. Surv., Bull.*, 34: 159–164.

SMITH, H. T. U., 1963. Eolian geomorphology, wind direction and climatic change in North Africa. *Air Force Cambridge Res. Lab., Project, 7628*: 49 pp.

SMITH, H. T. U., 1964. Periglacialeolian phenomena in the United States. *Rept. Intern. Conf. Quaternary, 6th*, 4: 177–186.

SMITH, H. T. U., 1965. Dune morphology and chronology in central and western Nebraska. *J. Geol.*, 73: 557–578.

SNYDER, C. T., 1967. Pleistocene Lakes in Western United States. 15 pp. (unpublished).

SNYDER, C. T. and LANGBEIN, W. B., 1962. The Pleistocene Lake in Spring Valley, Nevada, and its climatic implications. *J. Geophys. Res.*, 67: 2385–2394.

SOERGEL, W., 1937. *Die Vereisungskurve*. Borntraeger, Berlin, 87 S.

STAHL, J. B., 1959. The developmental history of the chironomid and *Chaoborus* faunas of Myers Lake. *Indiana Univ. Dept. Zool., Invest. Indiana Lakes Streams*, 5: 47–102.

STEARNS, C. E., 1942. A fossil marmot from New Mexico and its climatic significance. *Am. J. Sci.*, 240: 867–878.

STEARNS, H. T., 1941. Shore benches on north Pacific islands. *Bull. Geol., Soc. Am.*, 52: 773–780.

STEARNS, H. T., 1945a. Late geologic history of the Pacific basin. *Am. J. Sci.*, 243: 614–626.

STEARNS, H. T., 1945b. Eustatic shorelines in the Pacific. *Bull. Geol. Soc. Am.*, 56: 1071–1078.

STEPHENS, N. and SYNGE, F. M., 1966. Pleistocene shorelines. In: G. H. DURY (Editor), *Essays in Geomorphology*. Elsevier, Amsterdam, 1–52.

STEWART, O. C., 1953. Why the Great Plains are treeless. *Colo. Quarterly*, 2: 40–50.

STONE, R. O., 1956. *A Geologic Investigation of Playa Lakes*. Thesis, Univ. Southern Calif., Los Angeles, Calif., 302 pp. (unpublished).

STUIVER, M., 1964. Carbon isotopic distribution and correlated chronology of Searles Lake Sediments. *Am. J. Sci.*, 262: 377–392.

SVERDRUP, H. U., 1937. On the evaporation from the oceans. *J. Marine Res.*, 1: 3–14.

SVERDRUP, H. U., 1946. The humidity gradient over the sea surface. *J. Meteorol.*, 3: 1–8.

TANNER, W. F., 1965. Cause and development of an ice age. *J. Geol.*, 73: 413–430.

TATSUMOTO, M. and GOLDBERG, E. D., 1959. Some aspects of the marine geochemistry of uranium. *Geochim. Cosmochim., Acta*, 17: 201–208.

TAYLOR, D. W., 1960. Late Cenozoic molluscan faunas from the High Plains. *U.S., Geol., Surv., Profess. Papers*, 337: 94 pp.

TAYLOR, D. W., 1965. The study of Pleistocene nonmarine mollusks in North America. In: H. E. WRIGHT and D. G. FREY (Editors), *The Quaternary of the United States*. Princeton Univ. Press, Princeton, N.J., 597–611.

THORARINSSON, S., 1940. Present glacier shrinkage, and eustatic changes of sea-level. *Geograph. Ann.* 22: 131–159.

THORNWAITE, C. W. and HOLZMAN, B., 1939. The determination of evaporation from land and water surfaces. *Monthly Weather Rev.*, 67: 4–11.

THORPE, J. J. and SMITH, H. T. U., 1952. *Map of the Pleistocene Eolian Deposits of the United States. Map of Alaska, and Parts of Canada*. Geol. Soc. Am., New York, N.Y.

THORP, J., JOHNSON, W. M. and REED, E. C., 1951. Some post-Pliocene buried soils of central United States. *J. Soil Sci.*, 2: 1–19.

THURBER, D., 1962. Anamolous U^{234}/U^{238} in nature. *J. Geophys. Res.*, 67: 4518–4520.

THURBER, D., BROECKER, W. S., POTRATZ, H. A. and BLANCHARD, R. L., 1965. Uranium series ages of coral from Pacific atolls. *Science*, 149: 55–58.

TRICART, J., 1956a. France. *Biul. Peryglacjalny* 4: 117–138.

TRICART, J., 1956b. *Cartes des Phenomenes Periglaciaires Quaternaires en France*. Imprimerie Nationale, Paris.

TROLL, C., 1956. Die klimatypen an der schneegrenze. *Acta Congr. Intern. INQUA 4th, Rome, 1953*, pp.820–830.

UREY, H. C., LOWENSTAM, H. A., EPSTEIN, S. and McKINNEY, C. R., 1951. Measurement of paleotemperatures and temperatures of the Upper Cretaceous of England, Denmark, and the southeastern United States. *Bull. Geol. Soc. Am.*, 62: 399–416.

VALENTINE, J. W. and MEADE, R. F., 1960. Isotopic and zoogeographic paleotemperatures of California Pleistocene Mollusca. *Science*, 132: 810–811.

VALENTINE, J. W. and MEADE, R. F., 1961. Californian Pleistocene paleotemperatures. *Univ. Calif. (Berkeley) Publ., Geol. Sci.*, 40: 1–46.

VAN WOERKOM, A. J. J., 1953. The astronomical theory of climate changes. In: H. SHAPLEY (Editor), *Climatic Change, Evidence, Causes, and Effects*. Harvard Univ. Press, Cambridge, Mass., pp. 147–157.

VOIGHT, E., 1964. Zur temperatur-kurve der oberen Kreide in Europa. *Geol. Rundschau*, 54: 270–317.

WAYLAND, E. J., 1934. Rifts, rivers, rains, and early man in Uganda. *Roy. Anthropol. Inst. J.*, 64: 333–352.

WEBER, J. N., 1964. Paleoclimatic significance of δ-oxygen[18] time trends observed by oxygen isotopic analysis of freshwater limestones. *Nature*, 203: 969–970.

WELLINGTON, J. H., 1943. The Lake Chrissie problem. *S. African Geograph. J.*, 25: 50–64.

WELLINGTON, J. H., 1945. Notes on the drainage of the Western Free State Sandvild. *S. African Geograph. J.*, 27: 73–77.

WENDORF, F., 1961. *Paleoecology of the Llano Estacado*. Museum New Mexico Press, Santa Fe, N.M., 144 pp.

WENDORF, F. and HESTER, J. J., 1962. Early man's utilization of the Great Plains environment. *Am. Antiquity*, 28: 159–171.

WERTH, E., 1925. Die Pflanzenführenden Diluvial-ablagerungen der thuringischsachsichen Bucht. *Ber. Deut. Botan. Ges.*, 43.

WEXLER, H., 1952. Volcanoes and world climate. *Sci. Am.*, 186: 74–80.

WEXLER, H., 1953. Radiation balance of the earth as a factor in climatic change. In: H. SHAPLEY (Editor), *Climatic Change, Evidence, Causes, and Effects*. Harvard Univ. Press, Cambridge, Mass, pp.73–105.

WEXLER, H., 1960. Possible causes of climatic fluctuations. In: *Dynamics of Climate*. Pergamon, New York, N.Y., 93–95.

WHITNEY, J. D., 1882. *Climatic Changes of Later Geological Times*. Harvard Univ. Press, Cambridge, Mass, 394 pp.

WILHELMY, H., 1957. Eiszeit und Eiszeitklima in den feuchttropischen Anden. *Geomorphol. Studien*.

WILLETT, H. C., 1949. Long period fluctuations of the general circulation of the atmosphere. *J. Meteorol.*, 6: 34–50.

WILLETT, H. C., 1953. Atmospheric and oceanic circulation as factors in glacial-interglacial changes of climate. In: H. SHAPLEY (Editor), *Climatic Change, Evidence, Causes, and Effects*. Harvard Univ. Press, Cambridge, Mass., 51–71.

WILLETT, H. C., 1961. The pattern of solar-climatic relationships. *Ann. N.Y. Acad. Sci.*, 95: 89–106.

WILLETT, H. C., 1964. Evidence of solar-climatic relationships. In: L. M. THOMPSON (Editor), *Weather and on Food Supply*. Iowa State Univ., Ames, Iowa, pp.123–151.

WOLBACH, J., 1953. The insufficiency of geographical causes of climate change. In: H. SHAPLEY (Editor), *Climatic Change, Evidence, Cause, and Effects*. Harvard Univ. Press, Cambridge, Mass., pp.107–116.

WOLDSTEDT, P., 1954. Die allgemeinen Erscheinungen des Eiszeitalters. In: *Das Eiszeitalter*. Enke, Stuttgart, 1: 374 S.

WOLDSTEDT, P., 1958. Europa, Vorderasien, und Nordafrika im Eiszeitalter. In: *Das Eiszeitalter*. Enke, Stuttgart, 2.

WOLF, F. A., 1966a. Fungus spores in East African lake sediments. *Bull. Torrey Botan. Club*, 93: 104–113.

WOLF, F. A., 1966b. Fungus spores in East African lake sediments, 2. *J. Elisha Mitchell Sci. Soc.*, 82: 57–61.

WOLF, F. A. and CAVALIERE, S. C., 1966. Fungus spores in East African lake sediments, 3. *J. Elisha Mitchell Sci. Soc.*, 82: 149–154.

WRIGHT JR., H. E., 1961. Late Pleistocene climate of Europe—a review. *Bull. Geol. Soc. Am.*, 72: 933–984.

YOUNG, A. A., 1942. *Investigations of Evaporation from Screen Pan and Development of a Coefficient for the Conversion of Pan Evaporation to Lake Evaporation—U.S., Dept. Agr., Publ.*, 160 pp.

YOUNG, A. A., 1947a. Evaporation from water surfaces in California. *Calif., Dept. Water Resources, Bull.*, 54: 59 pp.

YOUNG, A. A., 1947b. Some recent evaporation investigations. *Trans. Am. Geophys. Union*, 28: 279–284.

ZEUNER, F. E., 1950. *Dating the Past*. Methuen, London, 474 pp.

ZEUNER, F. E., 1959. *The Pleistocene Period*, 2nd ed. Hutchison, London, 447 pp.

ZEUNER, F. E., 1961. The sequence of terraces of lower Thames and the radiation chronology. *Ann. N.Y. Acad. Sci.*, 95: 377–380.

INDEX[1]

---

[1] Only the page numbers where an author is mentioned are included here. Readers are referred to
the reference lists at the end of each Part.